Laboratory Activities Manual
Teacher Edition

earth.msscience.com

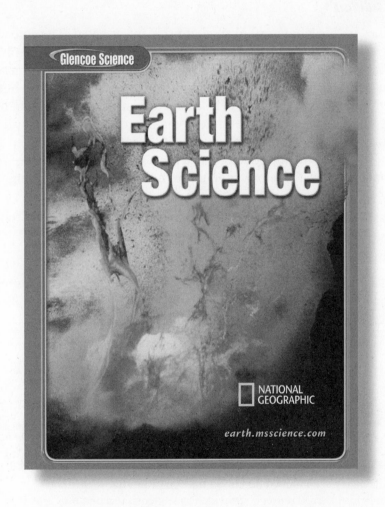

Glencoe Science

Earth Science

NATIONAL GEOGRAPHIC

earth.msscience.com

Mc Graw Hill **Glencoe**

New York, New York   Columbus, Ohio   Chicago, Illinois   Peoria, Illinois   Woodland Hills, California

To the Teacher

Activities in **Glencoe Earth Science Laboratory Activities Manual** do not require elaborate supplies or extensive pre-lab preparations. They are designed to explore science through a stimulating yet simple and relaxed approach to each topic. Helpful comments, suggestions, and answers to all questions are provided at the back of the **Teacher Edition.**

Activities in this laboratory manual are student-oriented. The scientific conclusions desired are not valid for any student unless he or she is directly involved in obtaining them. The activities should be performed by students only with your supervision. Directions are straightforward, so students can follow them easily. Students should be able to work through a problem to a satisfactory answer. The design of the manual is such that students should be interested enough to do their own investigating and not accept conclusions made by someone else. Students should discover their own mistakes through a review of the introductory statement, **Strategy,** and **Procedure.** If students still cannot reach a satisfactory conclusion, assistance in interpreting data may be needed.

Each activity can be torn from the book and handed in when the lab has been completed. Although the labs are not designed as a grading device, they can serve as a measure of progress for you and your students.

Most labs can be completed in a single class period. Some do not require the entire period; others require portions of two or more consecutive periods. Some require a preliminary setup followed by several inspections.

 **Glencoe**

The **McGraw·Hill** Companies

Send all inquiries to:
Glencoe/McGraw-Hill
8787 Orion Place
Columbus, OH 43240-4027

ISBN 0-07-866967-7

Printed in the United States of America.

4 5 6 7 8 9 10 113 09 08 07

Table of Contents

Inquiry in the Science Laboratory

What is inquiry?

The process of inquiry models actual science practice, encourages problem-solving strategies, and develops critical-thinking skills. Students are actively involved in the learning process when they determine materials, procedures, and the topics and questions they want to investigate.

Inquiry can range from a very structured activity for those students who need more guidance, to a more open-ended approach in which students design their investigations. We encourage you to modify the labs in this manual in a manner that best supports your students.

Why is inquiry important?

Inquiry activities, such as those in *Glencoe's Laboratory Activities Manual*, will help students develop educational, career, and life skills. Students learn how to think for themselves, how to solve problems, and how to apply prior knowledge to new situations.

How can this book help?

Glencoe's Laboratory Activities Manual is structured to give support to both teachers and students. Important scientific concepts are the core of each lab. Students gain practice in developing and testing their own hypotheses, designing experiments, gathering and analyzing data, and communicating their conclusions to their peers. Teachers are given strategies to guide students who need additional structure and to encourage students who are ready for more open-ended exploration.

Suggestions for Incorporating Inquiry in the Science Classroom

Inquiry in science does take extra time, just as it would in a research lab. Here are some ways you might be able to efficiently incorporate inquiry into your classroom.

- Supply various materials that are related to the concept you are trying to convey and allow students to explore them in groups for about 15 minutes. Have groups brainstorm ideas and list questions they have about those concepts. Have them list materials they will need. As a class or on your own, eliminate those questions that cannot be answered in the classroom. Gather any additional materials that are needed and allow students to begin their explorations the next day or the next week.

- Have students brainstorm questions they would like to explore. As a class, choose 1 or 2 reasonable questions that each group will explore in its own way. (This is very helpful if you are trying to cover a specific topic.)

- Give your students a more guided activity that relates hard-to-understand concepts and skills. Then, allow them to explore on their own with a wider variety of materials. Make sure you allow time for debriefing so the students (and you) will understand what they learned from the experience.

- Students will need practice doing inquiry before they should be allowed to explore completely on their own. Be sure to give them lots of practice in using the tools of science so that their explorations are more successful.

- Encourage students to rely on their data and not on what they think the answer should be. If their data are unexpected, help them to problem-solve what might have happened.

Developing Process Skills

Basic Process Skills

Observe: Students use one or more senses to learn more about objects and events.

Classify: Students group objects or events based on common properties and/or categorize based on existing relationships among objects or events.

Infer: Students propose interpretations, explanations, and causes from observed events and collected data.

Communicate: Students convey information verbally, both in oral and written forms, and visually through graphs, charts, pictures, and diagrams.

Measure in SI: Students identify length, area, volume, mass, and temperature to describe and quantify objects or events.

Predict: Students propose possible results or outcomes of future events based on observations and inferences drawn from previous events.

Calculate: Students transfer or apply ordering, counting, adding, subtracting, multiplying, and dividing to quantify data where appropriate.

Complex Process Skills

Interpret Data: Students explain the meaning of information gathered in scientific situations.

Form Hypotheses: Students make an informed assumption in order to draw out and test its logical consequences.

Experiment: Students test hypotheses or predictions under conditions in which variables are both controlled and manipulated.

Formulate Models: Students construct mental, verbal, or physical representations of ideas, objects, or events. The models are then used to clarify explanations or to demonstrate relationships.

Analyze Results: Students evaluate the outcome of an experiment to determine if it is reasonable. They should be able to draw conclusions and make inferences from the results.

Introducing/Reviewing Laboratory Work

Following proper techniques when using laboratory equipment helps prevent accidents and cuts down on the cost of replacement materials and devices. Students' success also is increased as their familiarity with the devices and their measurement and analysis skills increase. To facilitate student success in the classroom laboratory, first familiarize yourself with the general organization of Glencoe's science activities. The organization varies according to the type of activity. Then orient the students to the laboratory setting. This includes reviewing equipment and correct handling procedures with them, the use of SI units in their activities, and assessing their readiness for work in the laboratory.

Organization of Glencoe Science Laboratory Activities

- An **introductory statement** explains the science concepts involved in the activity. Specific information for the investigation of the problem is re-emphasized. This statement appears under the investigation title.

- A **strategy** or **list of objectives** provide objectives for student performance. If the student does not understand the goal(s) of the activity, a rereading of the section is advised.

- **Materials** is the list of all materials or possible materials needed for the activity. The **Materials** section should be previewed so that any supplies to be contributed by students may be obtained in advance. Be sure to assemble these materials *before* the beginning of a class period.

- A **safety precautions** section provides **icons** to prompt safety awareness and general **warning statement(s)** pertinent to the activity.

- Some labs include a section that states the **problem** or **what will be investigated**.

- Some labs have students state a **hypothesis**.

- **Procedure** is the step-by-step set of instructions for the activity. You may want to discuss the procedure with students before they begin the activity. Pre-activity discussions help prevent misuse of equipment and injuries that can result from careless use of the glassware, burners, and/or corrosive chemicals. Specific **safety warning statements** are placed appropriately in the **Procedure** section.

- **Data and Observations** includes sample graphs, charts, and tables to help improve students' analysis skills. Emphasis should be placed on the need to record all observations during and at the completion of the activity. In many cases, recorded data provide the necessary link in cause-and-effect relationships. Each student should do his or her own computations except in those activities where group work or class averages are required.

- An **analysis** or **questions and conclusions** section contains discussion questions and blanks for student answers at the end of each activity. These questions are designed to review main ideas, to direct attention to key parts of the procedure, and to relate the material to science concepts and applications. Answering these questions promotes and reinforces student learning.

- A **strategy check** or **hypothesis check** section allows students to evaluate the activity. If a student can place a checkmark in the blank provided, he or she has gained a skill, interpreted a concept, or learned a process.

Evaluating Activity Work

Evaluation of the activities and of the general outcomes of laboratory work is a difficult task. Pure recognition and recall tests are not usually suitable for evaluating laboratory experience. Evaluation methods that depend on accurate observation, recognition of pertinent data, and ability to reason logically are more suitable for measuring outcomes of laboratory work. This type of evaluation may be done through periodic checking of student notebooks or individual or group conferences. You may also require students to submit laboratory reports. Laboratory reports should include

- a clearly stated problem.
- a procedure outlined in detail.
- data organized in good form and understandable; may include
  - **a.** labeled diagrams.
  - **b.** labeled and titled graphs.
  - **c.** data tables.
- conclusions that answer the problem based on data obtained in the activity.
- a report that is clear enough to serve as a future review of the material.

The following questions should be answered in evaluating an activity report.
- Is the report written clearly enough so that an uninformed person could read it and know exactly what was being attempted, how it was done, and what conclusions were reached?
- Can the student duplicate the experiment using the report alone as a guide?

Achievement tests designed to assess understanding of course content are an important evaluation technique for laboratory work. Knowledge should be obtained through correct laboratory methods.
- You may wish to observe techniques used, correctness of procedures, and results obtained. An observational checklist based on objectives could be used.
- You may wish to direct students to perform a laboratory task in a practical test. Students should be able to satisfactorily complete this test before beginning laboratory work. For this test, set up equipment stations in the classroom. At each station, provide instructions.

Station 1: **Lighting a Laboratory Burner**
Equipment: laboratory burner, rubber hose, gas outlet, gas lighter or safety matches
Instructions: Correctly set up and light the burner and adjust the flame.

Station 2: **Decanting and Filtering**
Equipment: two beakers—one containing a mixture of water and sand; stirring rod; filter paper; funnel; ring stand
Instructions: Decant the clear liquid from the residue. Correctly set up the equipment for a filtration procedure.

Station 3: **Using the Balance**
Equipment: balance, rubber stopper
Instructions: Correctly carry the balance from Station 3 to your desk and back to Station 3. Determine the mass of the rubber stopper.

Evaluating Activity Work continued

Station 4: Measuring Temperature
Equipment: thermometer, beaker of water
Instructions: Position the thermometer correctly and determine the temperature of the water in the beaker.

Station 5: Measuring Volume
Equipment: graduated cylinder containing colored water
Instructions: Determine the volume of water in the graduated cylinder.

Station 6: Identifying Parts of a Microscope
Equipment: microscope, labels
Instructions: Correctly identify the labeled parts of this microscope.

Station 7: Using a Microscope
Equipment: microscope, prepared slide
Instructions: Correctly carry the microscope from Station 7 to your desk and back to Station 7. Place the slide on the stage and bring the slide into sharp focus.

Station 8: Inserting Glass Tubing into a Rubber Stopper
Equipment: glass tubing, glycerol or soapy water, one-hole rubber stopper, cloth towel
Instructions: Insert the glass tubing into the rubber stopper.

Introducing/Reviewing
Laboratory Safety Guidelines

Safe Laboratory Conduct

Whether you are a first-time or very experienced teacher, a review of safety guidelines is in order. This section deals with behaviors and actions that foster a safe learning environment. Because you serve as the role model for the behavior in the laboratory that you expect from your students, first review the safety guidelines for teachers. Then, on the first day of classes, introduce or review the safety guidelines that are the students' responsibility.

Teacher Safety Guidelines

- Thoroughly review your local safety regulations and this manual. Modify any activities to comply with your local regulations. For example, open flames are NOT permitted in some states or communities.

- Be trained in first aid and CPR.

- Be aware of students with allergies or other medical conditions that might limit their activities or require special protective equipment, such as facemasks.

- Have a list of substances to be used in lab activities made available to the doctor of any pregnant teacher or student so that limitations may be determined beforehand.

- NEVER leave students unattended in the classroom or field setting.

- NEVER be alone or out of earshot of someone when you prepare lab activities or equipment.

- Always wash your hands with antibacterial soap and warm water upon entering the laboratory, after live cultures have been handled, after cleanup, and before removing safety goggles.

- NEVER perform an investigation on any animal that might be a health hazard to humans or cause pain or suffering to the animal.

- Use protista and other invertebrates for lab or field activities involving animals when possible. Protista represent a wide variety of organisms and can be obtained in large quantities.

- A qualified adult supervisor who has had training in the proper care and handling of laboratory animals must assume responsibility for the conditions of any activity that involves living vertebrates. NO activity/investigation should be conducted that involves drugs, organisms pathogenic to humans or other vertebrates, ionizing radiation, surgical procedures, or carcinogens unless the procedures have been approved by and will be performed or supervised by a qualified biomedical scientist.

Teacher Safety Guidelines   continued

- Have students notify you beforehand if they plan to bring in a pet for observation.

- Instruct students about the hazards involved with wild animals and your school's policy and local and state laws regarding their capture and use in the classroom/laboratory. **WARNING:** *Wild animals may exhibit unpredictable behaviors, may become dangerous as they mature, and if declawed, may not be accepted by zoos and will probably die if released into the wild.* **WARNING:** *There is the potential of contracting rabies from any infected warm-blooded animal.*

- It is recomended that you purchase fumigated, steam sterilized materials. **WARNING:**

  - *Owl pellets can be a source of salmonella.*

  - *Bird nests contain many organisms that can cause diseases.*

  - *Bird eggs, even if disinfected when first acquired, will decay after a few days from gases building up in them. Rotten eggs produce noxious odors.*

  - *Some insects carry diseases that are serious if transmitted to humans.*

Presenting Safety Guidelines to Students

- Review the use and location of safety equipment, evacuation guidelines, and first aid procedures. Refer to fire drill regulations and a chart of emergency procedures, which should be posted in a prominent place in the laboratory. Assign safety partners and explain their role in helping during emergencies.

- Discuss safe disposal of materials and laboratory cleanup policy.

- Preview Glencoe's science activities with students and discuss the safety icons and their meanings (see p. 17). Point out the warning statements and the importance of heeding them. Distribute the Safety Symbols reference sheet (see p. 14).

- Distribute and discuss Student Laboratory and Safety Guidelines (see p. 15). Emphasize proper attitudes for working in the laboratory and field and review or present school rules regarding the consequences of misbehavior. Stress the need for safe practices on the part of everyone involved. Then distribute the Student Science Laboratory Safety Contract found on p. 16. You may wish to have each student and parent or guardian sign a safety contract at the beginning of each course. Review the safety guidelines and safety contract with students at least once a month.

Preparation of Solutions

It is important to use safe laboratory techniques when handling all chemicals. Many substances may appear harmless but are, in fact, toxic, corrosive, and very reactive. Always check with the supplier. Chemicals should never be ingested. Be sure to use proper techniques to smell solutions or other agents. Always wear safety goggles and an apron. Observe the following precautions.

1. Always add acids to water, never the reverse.
2. When sodium hydroxide is added to water, a large amount of thermal energy is released. Use extra care when handling this substance.
3. Poisonous/corrosive liquid and/or vapor. Use in fume hood if possible. Example: hydrochloric acid
4. Poisonous and corrosive to eyes, lungs, and skin. Examples: acids, silver nitrate, iodine, potassium permanganate
5. Poisonous if swallowed, inhaled, or absorbed through the skin. Example: silver compounds

Limewater solution: Add 1.5 g calcium hydroxide to 1 liter of water. Mix to dissolve. If necessary, filter to remove undissolved calcium hydroxide (limewater is a saturated solution of calcium hydroxide).

Ocean water (salt and water solution): For a 3.5% salt solution that simulates the concentration of ocean water, dissolve 35 g salt in 965 mL water.

Lab Preparation

Laboratory Equipment and Supplies

This table of equipment and inexpensive, easily accessible materials can help you prepare for your science class.

It is assumed that goggles, laboratory aprons, gloves, tap water, textbooks, paper, calculators, pencils, and pens are available for all activities.

Non-Consumables	
Item	**Experiments used in**
30 cm piece of uninsulated, heavy copper wire	5-2
air mattress	15-1
balance	1-1, 2-2, 5-1, 18-2, 19-2, 20-2
bar magnet	3-2
basketball	23-2
beaker	7-1
beaker tongs (or pliers)	17-2
beaker, 100-mL (3)	8-2, 18-1
beaker, 2000-mL, heat proof	2-2
beaker, 250-mL (2)	2-2, 3-2, 18-1
beaker, 500-mL	7-2, 9-1, 15-1, 20-2
beaker, 50-mL (2)	18-2
bicycle pump	15-1
binoculars or telescope (optional)	22-1
block diagram, Figure 1	13-1
books (or boxes)	24-2
brush, soft	12-1
Bunsen burner	5-1
cake tin with lid	12-1
can opener	7-2
cardboard base, 21.5 cm × 28 cm	8-2
cardboard, stiff	24-1
Celsius thermometer, metal backed	15-2
cereal bowl	21-1
clear plastic drinking glasses (2)	9-1
clear plastic storage box	18-1
clear plastic storage box and lid	24-1
clear plastic storage boxes (2)	18-2
clipboard	20-1
coat hangers (or bendable wire) (2)	21-1
colored marker	16-2

Non-Consumables (continued)

Item	Experiments used in
colored pencils	1-2, 4-2, 10-1, 11-1, 12-1, 13-1, 14-1, 14-2, 17-2, 18-2, 24-1
colored pencils, red and green	9-1
cork (or rubber stoppers with center holes) (2)	17-1
crucibles (2)	5-1
crystal system table in your textbook	3-1
dishpan (or sink)	7-2
dropper	4-1, 18-2
electric fan, small	24-2
felt-tip pen	7-2, 21-1, 22-2
flashlight	23-2
flashlight, small	25-1
flask, 250 mL	3-2
forceps (or tongs)	1-1
funnel	18-1
funnel, clear	3-2
glass funnels, small (2)	19-2
glass jars, each large enough to hold a funnel (2)	19-2
globe, mounted	22-2
globe, mounted on axis	23-1
glue (or paste)	16-2
graduated beaker	1-1
graduated beaker, 50-mL	3-2
graduated beaker, 500-mL	3-2
graduated cylinder	1-1, 7-1, 5-2, 16-1, 18-1
graduated cylinder, 25-mL	18-2
graduated cylinder, 50-mL	2-2
graduated cylinder, 50-mL	20-2
granite	2-1
granite, crushed	2-1
gravel	17-2
gravel, 1 L	8-1
grease pencil	18-2
half of a wood splint	5-2
hammer	5-1, 9-2
heat lamp	18-1
heat lamp, mounted	24-1
heat source	2-1, 2-2, 3-2
hemisphere, clear plastic (or terrarium top)	22-2
hot pad	5-1

Non-Consumables (continued)

Item	Experiments used in
hot plate	10-2, 17-2, 18-1
knife (or scissors)	19-1
list of data from teacher	21-2
magnifying lens	2-1, 4-2
map of the United States (or world atlas)	6-1
marker	12-2
measuring cup	12-2
measuring tape (or meter stick)	25-1
measuring tray	2-2
meterstick	6-2, 8-1, 12-2, 14-1, 14-2, 15-1, 23-1
metric ruler	1-1, 1-2, 5-1, 5-2, 7-2, 12-1, 18-1, 18-2, 19-1, 19-2
modeling clay (4 colors)	8-2
mouthed pot, medium-to-large	10-2
nail	9-2
nail, medium-sized	25-1
nails, iron	3-2
needle long enough to go through ball	16-2
numbered rock samples: gneiss, hornfels, marble, phyllite, quartzite, s ist, and soapstone	4-2
nut (or metal washer)	6-1
pan	2-2, 3-2, 9-1, 9-2
pan, larger than the circumference of the bag	21-1
pencils	3-1, 19-1, 20-1
pencils (2)	7-2
pie pans	3-2
pipe stem triangle	5-1
plant light (or gooseneck lamp with 150-watt bulb)	19-2
plastic bag, clear	21-1
plastic bucket	7-2, 8-1
plastic soda bottles, labels removed (2)	17-1
pointed stick (30 cm long)	7-2
protractor	8-1
protractor, Figure 2	6-1
ring stand with ring	5-1
rubber bands	25-1
ruler	24-2
scissors	1-2, 5-2, 6-1, 7-2, 9-1, 10-2, 12-2, 13-1, 16-2, 19-2, 23-2, 25-1, 25-2
shovel, small (or scoop)	13-2

Non-Consumables (continued)

Item	Experiments used in
small coffee cans with lids (2)	17-2
soft drink bottle, 2 L	16-1
soil	24-1
spoon	2-2, 4-1
sprinkling can	8-1
stirring rod	2-2
stopwatch	23-1
straight pin	1-2
straight pins, large (3)	5-2
stream table with hose	8-1
string	23-1
string to go around celestial equator	22-2
string with weight at one end (or small chain), should be at least 30 cm longer than depth of the box	19-1
sunlamp (or bright sunshine)	21-1
test tube	5-2
test tubes, 18-mm × 159-mm (2)	19-2
textbooks	12-2, 23-2
thermometer	5-2, 16-1, 24-1
thermometers, long chemistry-type (2) (or 100-watt light source, if no sunlight is available or apparatus for holding light source stationary)	17-1
thermometers, non-mercury (2)	17-2
thumbtack	6-1
timer	5-1
tongs	5-1, 10-2
watch glass (2)	18-1
watch with second hand	7-2, 17-2, 24-1
wood blocks (4)	8-1
world map (or globe showing longitude and time zones)	6-2

Consumables

Item	Experiments used in
adding machine tape, 4-4.5m	14-2
alcohol	1-1
aluminum foil	5-2
aluminum foil, 10 cm × 10 cm	18-2
balloons (9)	12-2
bituminous coal, small piece	5-1
calcite, clear and flat	3-1
cans of carbonated soft drinks (3)	9-2

Consumables (continued)

Item	Experiments used in
cardboard tubes of various sizes (should be at least 15 cm long)	19-1
cardboard, stiff	4-1, 6-1, 16-2
cardboard, thin	1-2, 7-2, 13-1
celery stalk with leaves	9-1
charcoal briquette	5-1
cheesecloth, 30 cm × 30 cm	7-2
clay	5-2, 13-2
clay, 1L	8-1
cold water	16-1
construction paper, black	25-1
construction paper, red, green or blue (the color should make water drops easy to see)	24-2
container, at least 25 cm × 20 cm × 15 cm (or approximately shoe-box size)	13-2
copper (II) sulfate crystals, $CuSO_4$	20-2
copper strip, dirty	7-1
corn syrup, white	3-2
egg	2-2
empty coffee can	12-2
filter papers (or coffee filters)	18-1
filter papers to fit funnel	3-2
fireplace matches	5-2
food coloring	4-1, 18-2
food coloring, red, blue, and green	12-2
freshwater (aged tap water)	18-2
glue	1-2, 6-1, 13-1
graph paper	1-2, 7-2, 14-1, 15-2, 16-2, 17-2, 21-2, 22-1, 24-1
gravel, 500 mL	7-2
ice cubes	1-1, 9-2
ice, crushed, not in cubes	24-2
iron (II) sulfate, $FeSO_4$	7-1
juice can, large	7-2
labels	19-2
large cardboard box with lid, should be 22 cm wide and 36 cm long (dark paper can be used instead of lid as a cover)	19-1
limewater (Ca(OH)2 solution)	9-2
litmus paper, blue	20-2

Consumables (continued)

Item	Experiments used in
masking tape	7-2, 19-1
matches	5-1, 16-1
mini-marshmallow	5-2
modeling clay	19-1
nails (iron scraps)	20-2
newspaper	5-1, 12-2, 13-2, 24-2
nylon line, 30 cm	16-2
objects to use in making trace fossils (3)	13-2
ocean water (salt water—make solution with salt and water)	18-2
old paintbrushes (3)	12-2
paper for labels	8-2
paper towels	17-1
patching plaster	4-1
peanut, shelled	5-2
pepper	3-2
pie pan, disposable	4-1, 7-1
pie pans, disposable (2)	2-1
piece of cardboard, small	23-2
piece of thick cardboard, approximately 50 cm × 50 cm	12-2
plaster of paris	12-2
plastic margarine tubs, 1 lb. (2)	12-2
plastic straw	6-1
plastic straw, flexible	9-2
polarizing film, with polarizing directions clearly marked (1)	3-1
red food coloring	9-1
rock salt	2-1
rock with a flat side	4-1
salt	2-2, 3-2, 7-1, 18-1
sand	3-2
sand, 1 L	8-1
sand, coarse	2-1, 18-1
sand, coarse, 0.5 L	9-1
sand, fine (or soil)	21-1
sand, fine, 500 mL	7-2
sand, not dirt	24-2
sheet of white paper with a single row of letters printed on it	3-1

Consumables (continued)

Item	Experiments used in
sheets of plastic foam wrap for padding packages (not made from corn or organic materials)	10-2
shirt button	1-2
silica powder (or borax)	12-1
slab clay	7-2
small tubes of toothpaste in different colors, white, green striped	12-2
sodium bicarbonate (baking soda)	19-2
soil	18-1
soil, 500 mL	7-2
sponge	12-2
string, 20 cm	6-1
table tennis ball	16-2
tape, adhesive	23-1
tape, clear	8-2, 13-1
toothpicks	8-2
varieties of "soil" (sand, potting soil, pea gravel, mulch, shredded dried leaves, fresh grass cuttings) (3)	13-2
vinegar, white	7-1
water	1-1, 2-1, 2-2, 3-2, 4-1, 5-2, 7-1, 7-2, 8-1, 9-1, 10-2, 12-2, 15-1, 17-1, 17-2, 20-2, 21-1
water which has stood at room temperature for at least 24 hours	19-2
water, distilled	18-1
water, very hot, but not boiling	16-1
waxed paper	4-1, 24-2
white correction fluid (or chalk or markers)	25-1
wooden paint stirrers (3)	12-2

Biologicals

Item	Experiments used in
Elodea, aquarium plant	19-2
flowers, several different kinds	12-1
No materials	11-2

Answers to Student Laboratory Equipment Worksheets

Figure 1

1. Graduated cylinders **2.** Florence flask **3.** Beakers **4.** Crucible **5.** Petri dish
6. Evaporating dish **7.** Erlenmeyer flask **8.** Long-stem funnel **9.** Watch glass

Figure 2

1. Test tubes **2.** Test-tube rack **3.** Square-bottomed test tubes **4.** Rubber stoppers
5. Corks **6.** Test-tube holder **7.** Test-tube brush

Figure 3

1. Utility clamp **2.** Wire gauze **3.** Metal ring **4.** Laboratory burner **5.** Gas inlet
6. Ring stand

Figure 4

1. Stirring rod **2.** Funnel

Figure 5

1. Thermometer **2.** Pipette **3.** Rubber tubing **4.** Pinch clamp **5.** Dropper **6.** Spatula
7. Stirring rod **8.** Triangular file **9.** Forceps **10.** Scalpel

Figure 6

1. Eyepiece **2.** Revolving nosepiece **3.** High-power objective lens **4.** Low-power
objective lens **5.** Stage **6.** Diaphragm **7.** Adjustment knob **8.** Light

Figure 7

1. Hickman still head **2.** Conical reaction vials **3.** Air reflux condenser **4.** Claisen head
5. Hirsch funnel **6.** Filter flask **7.** Erlenmeyer flask (10 mL) **8.** Funnel **9.** Reaction tubes
10. Magnetic stir bars **11.** Connector with support rod **12.** Pipette **13.** Stopper
14. Spatula **15.** Centrifuge tube **16.** Glass tube connectors **17.** Syringe **18.** Flasks
19. Tubing **20.** One-way stopcock **21.** Connectors **22.** Thermometer connectors

Figure 8

1. Berol pipettes **2.** Blue litmus vial and litmus discs **3.** Microstand **4.** Plastic tubing
(long and short) **5.** Zinc electrode **6.** Zinc coil **7.** Iron electrode **8.** Various tubes
9. Microspatulas **10.** Dual well comboplate **11.** Microburner **12.** Syringe
13. Chromatography paper strips **14.** pH color chart **15.** Gas collecting vial
16. Microcaps **17.** Compass **18.** Microlids **19.** Current LED indicator

Table of Contents

Getting Started

Science is the body of information including all the hypotheses and experiments that tell us about our environment. All people involved in scientific work use similar methods for gaining information. One important scientific skill is the ability to obtain data directly from the environment. Observations must be based on what actually happens in the environment. Equally important is the ability to organize these data into a form from which valid conclusions can be drawn. These conclusions must be such that other scientists can achieve the same results in the laboratory.

To make the most of your laboratory experience, you need to continually work to increase your laboratory skills. These skills include the ability to recognize and use equipment properly and to measure and use SI units accurately. Safety also must be an ongoing concern. To help you get started in discovering many fascinating things about the world around you, the next few pages provide you with:

- a visual overview of basic **laboratory equipment** for you to label
- a reference sheet of **SI units**
- a reference sheet of **safety symbols**
- a list of your **safety responsibilities** in the laboratory
- a **safety contract**

Each lab activity in this manual includes the following sections:

- an investigation **title** and introductory section providing information about the problem under study
- a **strategy** section identifying the **objective(s)** of the activity
- a list of needed **materials**
- safety concerns identified with **safety icons** and **caution statements**
- a set of step-by-step **procedures**
- a section to help you record your **data and observations**
- a section to help you **analyze your data** and record your **conclusions**
- a closing **strategy check** so that you can review your achievement of the objectives of the activity

Laboratory Equipment

Figure 1

1. _____

2. _____

3. _____

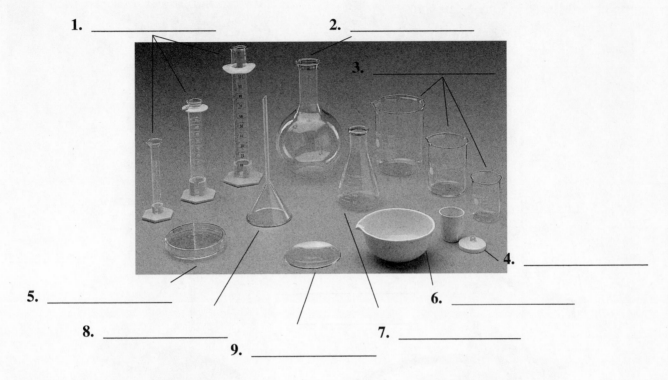

4. _____

5. _____

6. _____

7. _____

8. _____

9. _____

Figure 2

1. _____

2. _____

3. _____

4. _____

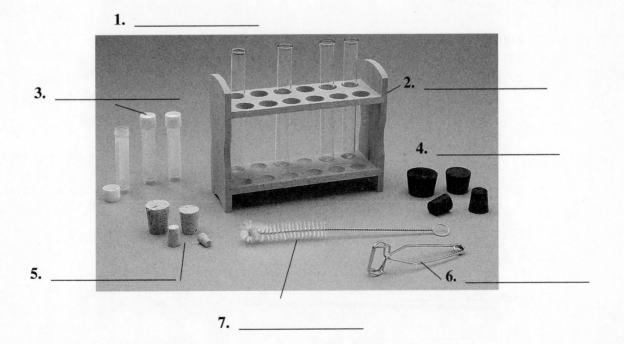

5. _____

6. _____

7. _____

Laboratory Equipment (continued)

Figure 3

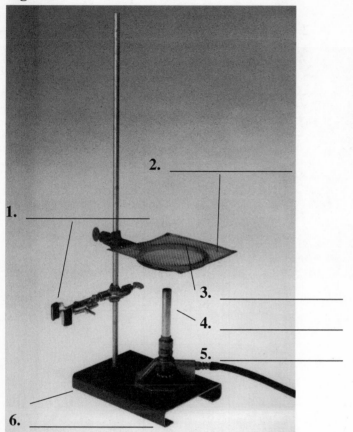

1. _____
2. _____
3. _____
4. _____
5. _____
6. _____

Figure 4

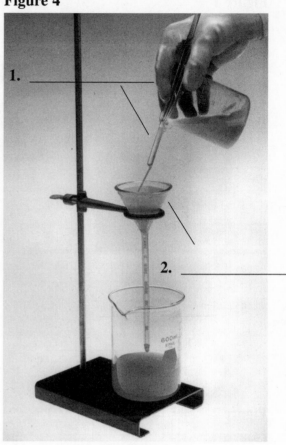

1. _____
2. _____

Figure 5

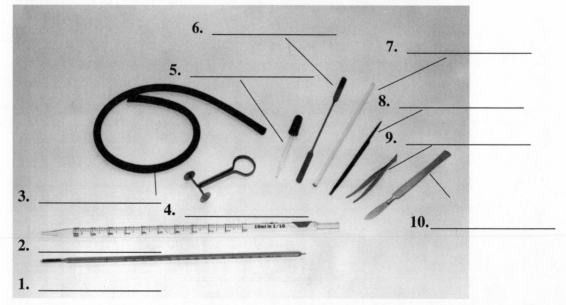

1. _____
2. _____
3. _____
4. _____
5. _____
6. _____
7. _____
8. _____
9. _____
10. _____

10ml in 1/10

Laboratory Equipment (continued)

Figure 6

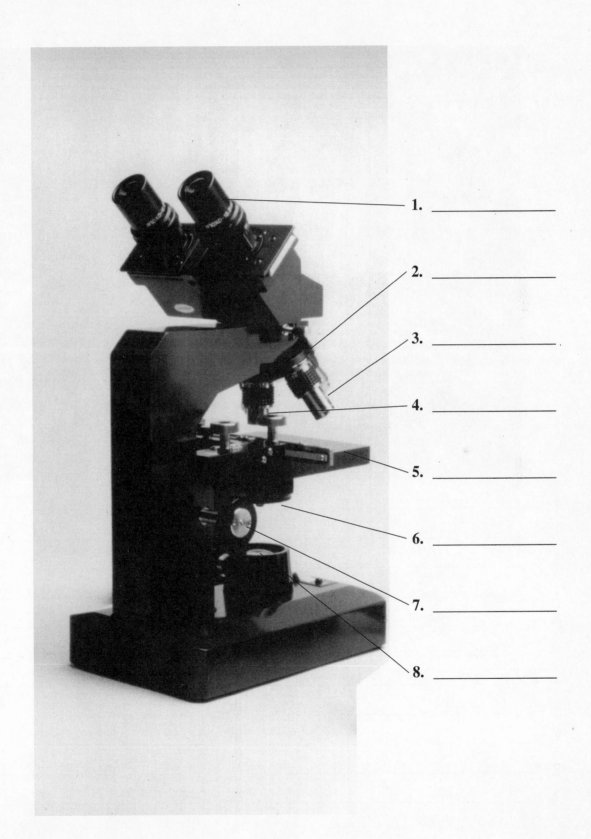

1. _____

2. _____

3. _____

4. _____

5. _____

6. _____

7. _____

8. _____

Laboratory Equipment (continued)

Figure 7

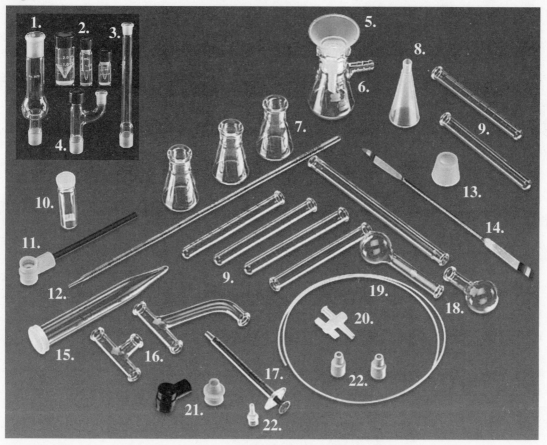

1. _____
2. _____
3. _____
4. _____
5. _____
6. _____
7. _____
8. _____
9. _____
10. _____
11. _____

12. _____
13. _____
14. _____
15. _____
16. _____
17. _____
18. _____
19. _____
20. _____
21. _____
22. _____

Laboratory Equipment (continued)

Figure 8

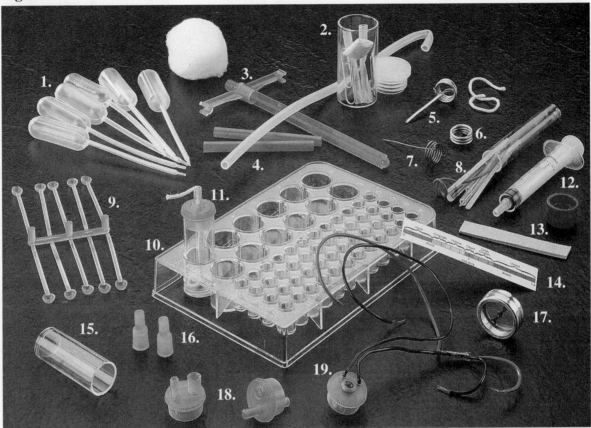

1. _____
2. _____
3. _____
4. _____
5. _____
6. _____
7. _____
8. _____
9. _____
10. _____

11. _____
12. _____
13. _____
14. _____
15. _____
16. _____
17. _____
18. _____
19. _____

SI Reference Sheet

The International System of Units (SI) is accepted as the standard for measurement throughout most of the world. Frequently used SI units are listed in **Table 1** and some supplementary SI units in **Table 2.**

Table 1

	Frequently Used SI Units
Length	1 millimeter (mm) = 100 micrometers (μm) 1 centimeter (cm) = 10 millimeters (mm) 1 meter (m) = 100 centimeters (cm) 1 kilometer (km) = 1,000 meters (m) 1 light-year = 9,460,000,000,000 kilometers (km)
Area	1 square meter (m²) = 10,000 square centimeters (cm²) 1 square kilometer (km²) = 1,000,000 square meters (m²)
Volume	1 milliliter (mL) = 1 cubic centimeter (cm³) 1 liter (L) = 1,000 milliliters (mL)
Mass	1 gram (g) = 1,000 milligrams (mg) 1 kilogram (kg) = 1,000 grams (g) 1 metric ton = 1,000 kilograms (kg)
Time	1 s = 1 second

Table 2

Supplementary SI Units			
Measurement	**Unit**	**Symbol**	**Expressed in base units**
Energy	joule	J	$kg \cdot m^2/s^2$
Force	newton	N	$kg \cdot m/s^2$
Power	watt	W	$kg \cdot m^2/s^3$ or J/s
Pressure	pascal	Pa	$kg/m \cdot s^2$ or $N \cdot m$

Sometimes quantities are measured using different SI units. In order to use them together in an equation, you must convert all of the quantities into the same unit. To convert, you multiply by a conversion factor. A conversion factor is a ratio that is equal to one. Make a conversion factor by building a ratio of equivalent units. Place the new units in the numerator and the old units in the denominator. For example, to convert 1.255 L to mL, multiply 1.255 L by the appropriate ratio as follows:

$$1.255 \text{ L} \times 1,000 \text{ mL}/1 \text{ L} = 1,255 \text{ mL}$$

The unit L cancels just as if it were a number.

Temperature measurements in SI often are made in degrees Celsius. Celsius temperature is a supplementary unit derived from the base unit kelvin. The Celsius scale (°C) has 100 equal graduations between the freezing temperature (0°C) and the boiling temperature of water (100°C). The following relationship exists between the Celsius and kelvin temperature scales:

$$K = °C + 273$$

SI Reference Sheet (continued)

To convert from °F to °C, you can:

1. For exact amounts, use the equation at the bottom of **Table 3**, or
2. For approximate amounts, find °F on the thermometer at the left of **Figure 1** and determine °C on the thermometer at the right.

Table 3

Figure 1

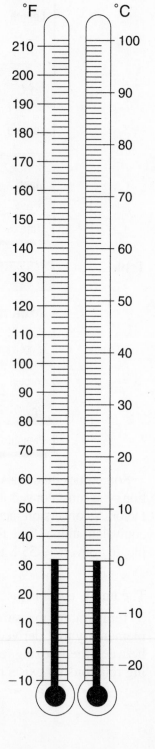

SI Metric to English Conversions			
	When you have:	**Multiply by:**	**To find:**
Length	inches	2.54	centimeters
	centimeters	0.39	inches
	feet	0.30	meters
	meters	3.28	feet
	yards	0.91	meters
	meters	1.09	yards
	miles	1.61	kilometers
	kilometers	0.62	miles
Mass and weight*	ounces	28.35	grams
	grams	0.04	ounces
	pounds	0.45	kilograms
	kilograms	2.20	pounds
	tons	0.91	metric tons
	metric tons	1.10	tons
	pounds	4.45	newtons
	newtons	0.23	pounds
Volume	cubic inches	16.39	cubic centimeters
	milliliters	0.06	cubic inches
	cubic feet	0.03	cubic meters
	cubic meters	35.31	cubic feet
	liters	1.06	quarts
	liters	0.26	gallons
	gallons	3.78	liters
Area	square inches	6.45	square centimeters
	square centimeters	0.16	square inches
	square feet	0.09	square meters
	square meters	10.76	square feet
	square miles	2.59	square kilometers
	square kilometers	0.39	square miles
	hectares	2.47	acres
	acres	0.40	hectares
Temperature	Fahrenheit	$\frac{5}{9}$ (°F − 32)	Celsius
	Celsius	$\frac{9}{5}$°C + 32	Fahrenheit

* Weight as measured in standard Earth gravity

SAFETY SYMBOLS

SAFETY SYMBOLS	HAZARD	EXAMPLES	PRECAUTION	REMEDY
DISPOSAL	Special disposal procedures need to be followed.	certain chemicals, living organisms	Do not dispose of these materials in the sink or trash can.	Dispose of wastes as directed by your teacher.
BIOLOGICAL	Organisms or other biological materials that might be harmful to humans	bacteria, fungi, blood, unpreserved tissues, plant materials	Avoid skin contact with these materials. Wear mask or gloves.	Notify your teacher if you suspect contact with material. Wash hands thoroughly.
EXTREME TEMPERATURE	Objects that can burn skin by being too cold or too hot	boiling liquids, hot plates, dry ice, liquid nitrogen	Use proper protection when handling.	Go to your teacher for first aid.
SHARP OBJECT	Use of tools or glassware that can easily puncture or slice skin	razor blades, pins, scalpels, pointed tools, dissecting probes, broken glass	Practice common-sense behavior and follow guidelines for use of the tool.	Go to your teacher for first aid.
FUME	Possible danger to respiratory tract from fumes	ammonia, acetone, nail polish remover, heated sulfur, moth balls	Make sure there is good ventilation. Never smell fumes directly. Wear a mask.	Leave foul area and notify your teacher immediately.
ELECTRICAL	Possible danger from electrical shock or burn	improper grounding, liquid spills, short circuits, exposed wires	Double-check setup with teacher. Check condition of wires and apparatus.	Do not attempt to fix electrical problems. Notify your teacher immediately.
IRRITANT	Substances that can irritate the skin or mucous membranes of the respiratory tract	pollen, moth balls, steel wool, fiberglass, potassium permanganate	Wear dust mask and gloves. Practice extra care when handling these materials.	Go to your teacher for first aid.
CHEMICAL	Chemicals can react with and destroy tissue and other materials	bleaches such as hydrogen peroxide; acids such as sulfuric acid, hydrochloric acid; bases such as ammonia, sodium hydroxide	Wear goggles, gloves, and an apron.	Immediately flush the affected area with water and notify your teacher.
TOXIC	Substance may be poisonous if touched, inhaled, or swallowed.	mercury, many metal compounds, iodine, poinsettia plant parts	Follow your teacher's instructions.	Always wash hands thoroughly after use. Go to your teacher for first aid.
FLAMMABLE	Flammable chemicals may be ignited by open flame, spark, or exposed heat.	alcohol, kerosene, potassium permanganate	Avoid open flames and heat when using flammable chemicals.	Notify your teacher immediately. Use fire safety equipment if applicable.
OPEN FLAME	Open flame in use, may cause fire.	hair, clothing, paper, synthetic materials	Tie back hair and loose clothing. Follow teacher's instruction on lighting and extinguishing flames.	Notify your teacher immediately. Use fire safety equipment if applicable.

 Eye Safety
Proper eye protection should be worn at all times by anyone performing or observing science activities.

 Clothing Protection
This symbol appears when substances could stain or burn clothing.

 Animal Safety
This symbol appears when safety of animals and students must be ensured.

 Handwashing
After the lab, wash hands with soap and water before removing goggles.

Student Laboratory and Safety Guidelines

Regarding Emergencies

- Inform the teacher immediately of *any* mishap—fire, injury, glassware breakage, chemical spills, and so forth.
- Follow your teacher's instructions and your school's procedures in dealing with emergencies.

Regarding Your Person

- Do NOT wear clothing that is loose enough to catch on anything and avoid sandals or open-toed shoes.
- Wear protective safety gloves, goggles, and aprons as instructed.
- Always wear safety goggles (not glasses) when using hazardous chemicals.
- Wear goggles throughout entire activity, cleanup, and handwashing.
- Keep your hands away from your face while working in the laboratory.
- Remove synthetic fingernails before working in the lab (these are highly flammable).
- Do NOT use hair spray, mousse, or other flammable hair products just before or during laboratory work where an open flame is used (they can ignite easily).
- Tie back long hair and loose clothing to keep them away from flames and equipment.
- Remove loose jewelry—chains or bracelets—while doing lab work.
- NEVER eat or drink while in the lab or store food in lab equipment or the lab refrigerator.
- Do NOT inhale vapors or taste, touch, or smell any chemical or substance unless instructed to do so by your teacher.

Regarding Your Work

- Read all instructions before you begin a laboratory or field activity. Ask questions if you do not understand any part of the activity.
- Work ONLY on activities assigned by your teacher.
- Do NOT substitute other chemicals/substances for those listed in your activity.
- Do NOT begin any activity until directed to do so by your teacher.
- Do NOT handle any equipment without specific permission.
- Remain in your own work area unless given permission by your teacher to leave it.
- Do NOT point heated containers—test tubes, flasks, and so forth—at yourself or anyone else.
- Do NOT take any materials or chemicals out of the classroom.
- Stay out of storage areas unless you are instructed to be there and are supervised by your teacher.
- NEVER work alone in the laboratory.
- When using dissection equipment, always cut away from yourself and others. Cut downward, never stabbing at the object.
- Handle living organisms or preserved specimens only when authorized by your teacher.
- Always wear heavy gloves when handling animals. If you are bitten or stung, notify your teacher immediately.

Regarding Cleanup

- Keep work and lab areas clean, limiting the amount of easily ignitable materials.
- Turn off all burners and other equipment before leaving the lab.
- Carefully dispose of waste materials as instructed by your teacher.
- Wash your hands thoroughly with soap and warm water after each activity.

Student Science Laboratory Safety Contract

I agree to:

- Act responsibly at all times in the laboratory.

- Follow all instructions given, orally or in writing, by my teacher.

- Perform only those activities assigned and approved by my teacher.

- Protect my eyes, face, hands, and body by wearing proper clothing and using protective equipment provided by my school.

- Carry out good housekeeping practices as instructed by my teacher.

- Know the location of safety and first aid equipment in the laboratory.

- Notify my teacher immediately of an emergency.

- NEVER work alone in the laboratory.

- NEVER eat or drink in the laboratory unless instructed to do so by my teacher.

- Handle living organisms or preserved specimens only when authorized by my teacher, and then, with respect.

- NEVER enter or work in a supply area unless instructed to do so and supervised by my teacher.

[This portion of the contract is to be kept by the student.]

[Return this portion to your teacher.]

I, _____, [print name] have read each of the statements in the Student Science Laboratory Safety Contract and understand these safety rules. I agree to abide by the safety regulations and any additional written or verbal instructions provided by the school district or my teacher. I further agree to follow all other written and verbal instructions given in class.

_____   _____
Student Signature   Date

I acknowledge that my child/ward has signed this contract in good faith.

_____   _____
Parent/Guardian Signature   Date

Problem Solving and a Scientific Method

Think back to the last problem you had to solve. You probably used some or all of the steps of a "Scientific Method." A scientific method is a logical approach to solving problems. Most scientists recognize four basic problem solving steps: (1) determining the problem, (2) testing, (3) analyzing the results, and (4) drawing conclusions.

Strategy

You will use the scientific method to determine the density of an ice cube.

Materials

ice cubes	graduated cylinder
graduated beaker	alcohol
metric ruler	balance
forceps or tongs	water

WARNING: *Do not ingest alcohol or breathe fumes. Some alcohol is poisonous. Liquid and vapor are extremely flammable.*

Procedure

1. In order to solve the problem, you must first determine what it is you need to know. Place an ice cube on the tabletop and make observations. Describe the shape of the ice cube. Using a metric ruler, measure its size. Record them in the data table below.

2. What other information is helpful that cannot be gained from initial observation? You may wish to do some research.

   A. Define the unknown terms:

   Density _____

   _____

   Mass _____

   _____

   Volume _____

   _____

3. Design a test (in this case a procedure) that will enable you to determine the density of an ice cube. Record the steps below. If you need a second trial, record that procedure also.

Ice cube	Observation
A. View on tabletop for 5 minutes	
B. Shape	
C. Size	
D. In water	
E. In alcohol	

First Trial Procedure

A. _____

B. _____

C. _____

D. _____

E. _____

Laboratory Activity 1 (continued)

Second Trial Procedure

A. _____

B. _____

C. _____

D. _____

E. _____

Data Collected (framework for writing results)

A. Volume of the ice cube: _____ cubic centimeters (cm³)

B. Mass of the ice cube: _____ grams (g)

C. Density of the ice cube: _____ grams/cubic centimeter (g/cm³)

4. Analyze the results.

A. My answer for the density of the ice cube was _____.

B. The accepted value for the density of the ice cube is _____.

C. Now determine the percent error. The percent error is determined by the following formula:

Accepted Value minus Calculated Value divided by the Accepted Value times 100.

$$\text{Accepted} - \frac{\text{Calculated}}{\text{Accepted} \times 100}$$

D. The percent error is _____.

Conclusion

If your percent error is low (under 10%), then your experimental design is acceptable given the materials and the time you had available for completing the task. Knowing the "right" answer to a problem is not always possible. A scientist has to repeat an experiment several times and often will compare the results with others.

5. Did you compare your results with the other students? _____

Did you compare procedures? _____

Do you think you need to change your procedures? _____

What is your conclusion? _____

Strategy Check

_____ Can you recognize the steps of a scientific method?

_____ Can you use a scientific method to determine the density of an ice cube?

Probability

Crystals in rocks and cells in plants and animals develop in relatively predictable ways. Other materials behave in unpredictable ways. Gas particles, for instance, move in every direction, bump into obstacles, then fly off in different directions. Scientists make educated guesses about this type of behavior based on the laws of probability. Studying probability helps scientists predict random behavior. Scientists make many observations of the random behavior and find the average of all these observations. They use this average to make predictions about how the material is likely to behave in the future.

Strategy

You will use a spinner to determine the direction and distance you will move.
You will use probability to interpret your random movements.

Materials

cardboard (thin)
glue or paste
scissors
straight pin
shirt button
pencils (colored)
graph paper
metric ruler

Procedure

1. Paste the spinner and pointer section, Figure 1, to the cardboard.
2. Cut out the spinner and the pointer.
3. Push the straight pin upward through the center dot of the spinner.
4. Place the button on the pin and then push the pin through the center of the arrow.
5. Spin the arrow. When it stops, read from the outer dial the direction in which you are to move. Record the direction in **Table 1** on the next page.
6. Spin the arrow again. When it stops, read the number of spaces you are to move from the inner dial. Record the number of spaces in **Table 1**.
7. Record 20 turns (2 spins each turn). This is Trial 1.

8. Spin 20 more turns; record under Trial 2. Spin 20 more turns; record under Trial 3.
9. Start at Point A at the center of the graph paper, and plot your movements for Trial 1. Move diagonally if the direction is northeast, southeast, northwest, or southwest. Move along a grid line if the direction is north, south, east, or west.
10. Using different colored pencils, plot your movements for Trials 2 and 3. Begin plotting each trial at Point A.
11. Measure and record the distances along a straight line from Point A to the end of your random paths. Record the class average also.

Laboratory Activity 2 (continued)

Data and Observations

Table 1

Turns	Trial 1		Trial 2		Trial 3	
	Direction	Spaces	Direction	Spaces	Direction	Spaces
1						
2						
3						
4						
5						
6						
7						
8						
9						
10						
11						
12						
13						
14						
15						
16						
17						
18						
19						
20						
Distance	■		■		■	
Class average distance	■		■		■	

Laboratory Activity 2 (continued)

Questions and Conclusions

1. Were the three distances equal?

_____

Did all three paths follow the same direction?

_____

2. Based on your three trials, can you make an accurate prediction of the distance and direction of future paths?

_____

3. Would the average distance of ten paths be more accurate for predicting distance and direction than the average of your three paths?

_____

Why?

_____

_____

4. How does the class average compare to your average?

_____

5. Which is the better prediction, the class average or your average? Explain.

_____

_____

6. Is a scientific law based on probability necessarily incorrect?

_____

Strategy Check

_____ Can you predict how far from Point A you will travel based on your three paths?

_____ Can you predict random motion using probability?

Laboratory Activity 2 (continued)

Figure 1

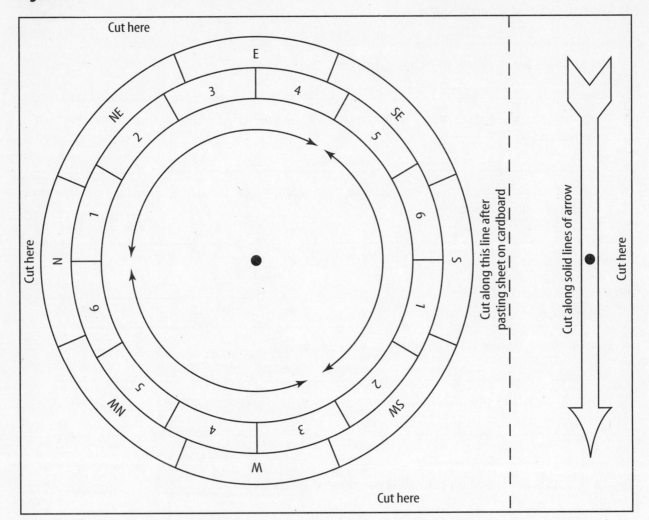

Mixtures and Compounds

Chapter 2

Matter is anything that has mass and occupies space. Matter exists in different forms. Three forms of matter are well known to us—elements, mixtures, and compounds. Elements are the basic materials of our world. Elements in a mixture have recognizable boundaries and can be separated by mechanical means. Elements that form a chemical compound can be separated only by a chemical process. Oxygen (O) is an element, which combined with hydrogen forms water, H_2O, a compound. Salt water is a mixture of two compounds, water and salt.

Strategy

You will separate a mixture into its parts.
You will compare the characteristics of a compound and a mixture.

Materials

granite   heat source   2 pie pans (disposable)   sand (coarse)
granite (crushed)   magnifying glass   rock salt   water

Procedure

1. Use the magnifying glass to observe the sand and granite. Sketch the shapes of the different minerals found in the granite and the shapes of the sand grains under Sketch A.
2. Sort the crushed granite into separate piles according to color.
3. Sketch the general shape of a piece from each pile of the sorted granite and label it as to color under Sketch B.
4. Mix a spoonful of sand in some water in a pie pan. Sketch what you observed under Sketch C.

5. Examine and sketch the salt crystals under Sketch D.
6. Mix a spoonful of salt in some water in the second pie pan. Record your observations.
7. Heat both pans until the water is evaporated. Sketch what is left in each pan under Sketch E.
   WARNING: *Be careful not to get clothes or hair close to the heat source.*

Data and Observations

Sketch A

Sketch B

Sketch C

Laboratory Activity 1 (continued)

Sketch D

Sketch E

Questions and Conclusions

1. Are any of the sand grains similar to any of the granite fragments? If so, describe them.

_____

_____

2. How are saltwater and sand and water similar? How are they different?

_____

_____

3. Is salt water a compound or mixture? Explain.

_____

_____

_____

4. Is granite a compound or mixture? Explain.

_____

_____

_____

5. Name some mechanical processes used to separate mixtures.

_____

_____

_____

Strategy Check

_____ Can you separate components of a mixture?

_____ Can you compare the characteristics of a compound and a mixture?

Density and Buoyancy

Density is the mass per unit of volume. Buoyancy involves mass and volume. The buoyant force is the upward push exerted on an object by a liquid. When the mass of the displaced liquid is equal to the mass of the object, the object floats.

Strategy

You will determine the densities of freshwater, salt water, and an egg.
You will deduce the relationship between density and buoyancy.

Materials

balance
beakers (250-mL and 2000-mL, heat proof)
egg
graduated cylinder (50-mL)

heat source
measuring tray
pan
salt

spoon
stirring rod
water

Procedure

1. Using the balance, measure out 25 grams of salt.
2. Heat 1 liter of water in the pan. Dissolve the salt in the water.
3. Pour the salt water into the 2000-mL beaker and let it cool to room temperature.
4. Determine the mass of 10 mL of the salt water. Record it in the table. Pour the salt water back into the beaker.
5. Determine the mass of 10 mL of freshwater at room temperature. Record it in the table.

6. Determine the mass of the egg. Record it in the table.
7. Determine the volume of the egg. Record it in the table.
8. Carefully pour 250 mL of freshwater on top of the cool salt water. Pour the water down the side of the beaker using the stirring rod. *Do not mix.*
9. Slip the egg into the beaker using the spoon. Observe and record its position.
10. Stir the solution, and observe what happens to the egg.

Data and Observations

	Mass (g)	Volume (cm³)	Density (g/cm³)
1. salt water		10	
2. freshwater		10	
3. egg			

Laboratory Activity 2 (continued)

Questions and Conclusions

1. Calculate the density of the freshwater, salt water, and egg. Show your work.

   Record the densities in the table under Data and Observations.

2. What happened to the egg when you added it to the separated freshwater and salt water?

   _____

   _____

3. Compare the density of the egg to that of the freshwater and the salt water.

   _____

   _____

4. What happened to the egg after you mixed the salt water and freshwater together?

   _____

   _____

5. State the relationship between density and buoyancy.

   _____

   _____

6. Explain, in terms of density, why a person is able to float in water.

   _____

   _____

7. Is it easier for a person to float in seawater or in freshwater? Why?

   _____

   _____

   _____

8. Explain how a balloon inflated with helium floats in the air.

   _____

   _____

   _____

Strategy Check

_____ Can you determine densities experimentally?

_____ Can you state the relationship between density and buoyancy?

LAB 1 Laboratory Activity

Minerals and Optical Crystallography

Rays of white light are waves that vibrate to produce a waveform in all directions, as shown in Figure 1. The vibrations move at 90-degree angles to the direction that the light rays are traveling. Light rays can be forced to vibrate along a single direction, or planar surface, if passed through a polarizing filter, as shown in Figure 2. We say that the light in Figure 2 is plane polarized.

When light passes through a crystal, the atoms in that crystal influence the behavior of the light rays.

For all crystals except those belonging to the cubic crystal system, the light is broken into two or more unique rays, each with its own velocity. Crystals that make the two rays are called *anisotropic*, and the rays are made because atoms are arranged differently in different directions in these crystals. Cubic crystals, on the other hand, are *isotropic*; atoms are arranged the same way in all directions, and the light is not split into two distinct rays.

Strategy

You will analyze the behavior of light rays in a crystal.
You will learn to use polarizing film to absorb light rays traveling in distinct directions.

Materials

calcite (clear and flat)
sheet of white paper with single row of letters printed on it
pencil
polarizing film (1 piece), with polarizing directions clearly marked
crystal system table in your textbook

Procedure

WARNING: *Do not taste, eat, or drink any materials used in the lab. If you are given epsom salts and salol (phenyl salicylate) crystals to examine, handle with care. Do not inhale the fumes.*

1. Place a clear, flat piece of calcite on top of a sheet of paper with a single row of letters printed on the paper. Be sure that the calcite is covering at least two of the letters on the paper. Sketch the image of the letters in Table 1.

2. Place a polarizing film on top of the calcite.

3. Rotate the film so that its polarizing direction, or the direction along which light rays are plane polarized, is parallel to the row of letters. Sketch the image of the letters in Table 1.

4. Rotate the film so that the polarizing direction is at a 90-degree angle to the letters. Sketch the image of the letters in Table 1.

Figure 2

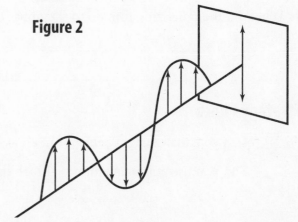

Figure 1

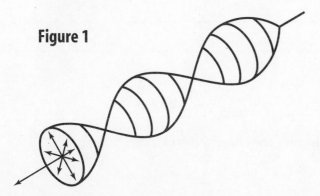

Laboratory Activity 1 (continued)

Data and Observations

Table 1

Orientation of polarizing film	Sketch of letter image
No film	
Polarizing direction parallel to letters	
Polarizing direction at 90° to letters	

Questions and Conclusions

1. What effect did the calcite crystal alone have on the row of letters on your paper?

_____

_____

2. How was the effect you described in your answer to question 1 produced?

_____

_____

3. Explain how a halite crystal could produce the effect referred to in question 1.

_____

_____

_____

_____

4. What did the polarizing film do to the image of the letters in steps 3 and 4?

_____

_____

Strategy Check

_____ Can you analyze light behavior in an anisotropic crystal?

_____ Can you use polarizing film to absorb light rays traveling in distinct directions?

Removal of Waste Rock

If a substance is to be classified as an ore, it must be extracted, processed, and sold at a profit. The substance may be a single mineral or a group of minerals. Without profit, no one can continue in the mining business. In general, mining and treating ores yields only a small amount of the valuable mineral product compared to the large amounts of waste rock handled during the operation.

Waste rock is removed from ore by both physical and chemical processes. Sometimes the ore is crushed and the waste rock is picked out by hand. Usually, however, other processes are used. Magnetic minerals can be separated from waste rock by using large magnets. In some cases, such as panning for gold, the waste rock floats away. Some minerals are lighter than the waste rock. They can be recovered by allowing unwanted rock to sink.

Strategy

You will use several of the methods industry employs to separate the wanted from the unwanted material.

You will remove iron by magnetism.

You will separate salt by filtering and distilling.

You will use gravity to separate minerals from waste rock.

Materials

sand
nails (iron)
pie pans
bar magnet

50-mL graduated cylinder
salt
pepper
500-mL beaker

250-mL beaker
water
filter papers to fit funnel
funnel (clear)

250-mL flask
pan
heat source
corn syrup (white)

Procedure

1. Mix the sand and nails together in a pie pan. Write down two ways of separating them in Table 1.

2. Draw the bar magnet across the bottom of the pan. When the nails are assembled in one area, remove them by drawing the magnet over their surface.

3. Mix together approximately 125 mL salt and 50 mL pepper in 500 mL beaker. Write down two methods of separating them in Table 1.

4. Add 250 mL of water to the solution of salt and pepper. Place a filter paper in the funnel, and then place the funnel in the flask. Pour the salt and pepper solution through the filter paper into the flask.

5. Allow the filter paper to dry. Observe and record your observations in the table.

6. Pour the liquid in the flask into the pan and boil the water off. In the table, record what sediment remains.

7. Place a clean filter in the funnel. Put the funnel in the flask and pour 50 mL of corn syrup into the funnel. Add a mixture of two or three nails and 15 mL of sand.

8. Allow the funnel to stand for about 15 min. Diagram the position of the sand and nails in the table.

Laboratory Activity 2 (continued)

Data and Observations
Table 1

Ways to separate sand and nails:	Sediment remaining after water is boiled off:
1.	6.
2.	Diagram of the position of sand and nails in the funnel:
Ways to separate salt and pepper:	7.
3.	
4.	
Filter paper observations:	
5.	

Questions and Conclusions

1. Which separation depends on gravity? Explain. _____

_____

2. Which method for separating iron from sand works better?

_____

3. When you mix pepper and salt, do you form a compound or a mixture?

_____

4. Is a mixture more like a rock or a mineral? Explain.

_____

5. After you pour the salt, pepper, and water solution through the funnel, what does the filter

paper look like? Explain. _____

_____

6. Which of the processes that you used is the filtration method of separation?

_____

7. Which process is the extraction method? _____

8. Which process is the evaporation method? _____

Strategy Check

_____ Can you separate salt from pepper? From water?

_____ Can you separate iron from sand by two different methods?

Concretions

Concretions are features found in sedimentary rocks. They may be spheres or flattened ovals. Concretions are formed when successive layers of cementing material are deposited and precipitated around a central core. Concretions may be harder than the surrounding rock. They are found as the surrounding rock is weathered.

Strategy

You will make a concretion.
You will observe the process of precipitation.
You will demonstrate the process by which some sedimentary rocks are formed.

Materials

waxed paper
cardboard (stiff)
pie pan (disposable)
spoon
patching plaster
water
rock with flat side
dropper
food coloring

Procedure

1. Place a piece of waxed paper on a piece of cardboard.
2. In the pie pan, mix some plaster with water. Add the water drop by drop until the plaster will spread but not run.
3. Place the rock flat side down on the waxed paper. Spread the plaster over its exposed sides. Record the color of the layer in Table 1.
4. Clean the pie pan thoroughly.
5. Place the rock in a location where it can dry undisturbed.
6. On the second day, repeat steps 3 through 5. Mix a drop of food coloring in the plaster. Record the color of the layer in Table 1. Let dry.
7. On the third day, add another layer using a different color. Record the color in the table.
8. On the fourth day, add another layer using a third color. Record. Contours may be thicker in some places since concretions are not always smooth.
9. On the fifth day, remove the cardboard and waxed paper. Sketch the bottom of the concretion on the next page.

Data and Observations

Table 1

Day	Color	Day	Color
1		3	
2		4	

Laboratory Activity 1 (continued)

Sketch of concretion

```
┌─────────────────────────────┐
│                             │
│                             │
│                             │
│                             │
│                             │
│                             │
└─────────────────────────────┘
```

Questions and Conclusions

1. What do the different layers represent?

_____

_____

_____

2. What causes the different layers in naturally formed concretions?

_____

_____

_____

3. Sometimes fossil hunters crack concretions open. Why do you think they do that?

_____

_____

_____

Strategy Check

_____ Can you make a concretion?

_____ Can you observe the process of precipitation?

_____ Can you demonstrate how some sedimentary rocks are formed?

LAB 2 Laboratory Activity

Identifying Metamorphic Rocks

Chapter 4

Metamorphic rocks are those which have been changed by heat, pressure, fluids, and chemical activity beneath Earth's surface. Each metamorphic rock can be identified and classified by its composition and texture. Foliated metamorphic rocks have a sheetlike or layering orientation of their minerals. Nonfoliated metamorphic rocks are composed of mineral grains that don't form layers. In this activity, you will examine and identify samples of both types of metamorphic rocks.

Strategy

You will describe the physical properties of various metamorphic rocks.
You will use a key to identify metamorphic rock samples.
You will group rocks into foliated and nonfoliated samples.

Materials

numbered rock samples: gneiss, hornfels, marble, phyllite, quartzite, schist, slate, and soapstone
magnifying lens
colored pencils

Safety Precautions

Procedure

1. Arrange your rock samples in numerical order. Begin by examining rock sample 1. In the table in the Data and Observations section, make a sketch of the rock sample. Use colored pencils to make your sketch as realistic as possible.

2. Next observe the rock's physical properties, such as the color and the size and arrangement of crystals. Write a description of the rock in the data table.

3. Use the identification key in Figure 1 to identify the name of the rock sample. Write the name in the data table.

4. Based on your observations and what you know about metamorphic rocks, classify the rock sample as foliated or nonfoliated. Record your classification in the data table.

5. Repeat steps 1 through 4 with rock samples 2 through 8.

Figure 1

Rock	Description
Gneiss	Alternating bands of light and dark minerals; bands may or may not be bent; often visible crystals; may contain thin, dark streaks
Hornfels	Usually dark in color, but may be pink, brown, violet, or green; fine-grained, dense, hard rock
Marble	Can be white, brown, red, green, or yellow; can be scratched with a nail; texture can be smooth or sugary; large interlocking cystals
Phyllite	Fine-grained rock; has a frosted sheen resembling frosted eye shadow
Quartzite	Made of interlocking quartz crystals; pure quartzite is white, but other minerals may color it gray or even black; scratches glass
Schist	Medium-grained rock; may have long, stretched crystals; may shimmer or look flaky
Slate	Usually gray or black; very fine-grained rock; individual grains difficult to see with hand lens; has obvious layers
Soapstone	Soft, easily carved rock; slippery feel; color varies from very pale to dark green

Laboratory Activity 2 (continued)

Data and Observations

Sample Number	Drawing	Description	Rock Name	Foliated or Nonfoliated
1				
2				
3				
4				
5				
6				
7				
8				

Questions and Conclusions

1. Which rock samples were the most difficult to identify?

_____

2. Suggest why two samples of the same type of metamorphic rock might look different from each other.

_____

_____

Strategy Check

_____ Can you describe the physical properties of various metamorphic rocks?

_____ Can you use a key to identify metamorphic rock samples?

_____ Can you group rocks into foliated and nonfoliated samples?

LAB 1 Laboratory Activity — Efficiency of Fossil Fuels

Plants use light energy from the Sun to produce energy-containing molecules. While some plants are burned directly to release that energy, other plants have undergone changes. Charcoal is made from wood that has been heated without the presence of oxygen, and it retains its energy-containing molecules. Plants that die and are covered by more plants, water, and sediment change first from peat to lignite, then to bituminous coal, and finally to anthracite coal. Heat and pressure cause these changes. The more heat and pressure that have been applied, the more concentrated the carbon content and the greater the energy-producing content of the deposit is. In this activity, you will examine how the properties of charcoal and bituminous coal compare.

Strategy

You will compare the burning times of charcoal and bituminous coal.

You will compare the amounts of residue produced from the burning of charcoal and bituminous coal.

You will infer which fuel is more efficient.

Materials

ring stand with ring
pipe-stem triangle
crucibles (2)
Bunsen burner
balance

metric ruler
bituminous coal, small piece
newspaper
hammer
matches or striker

timer
tongs
hot pad
charcoal briquette

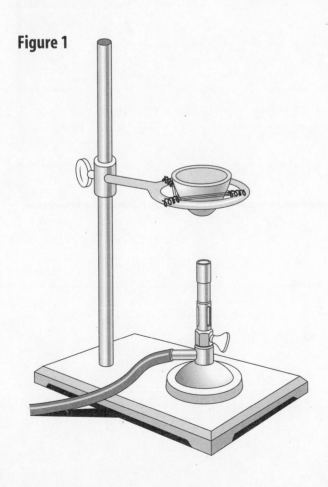

Figure 1

Procedure

1. Set up the ringstand, ring, pipe-stem triangle, a crucible, and Bunsen burner as shown in Figure 1. The top of the Bunsen burner should be about 5 cm below the bottom of the crucible.

2. Remove the crucible from the set-up. Use the balance to determine the mass of the crucible. Record its mass in the Data and Observations table.

3. Wrap the piece of coal in several layers of newspapers. Use a hammer to crush the sample. **WARNING:** *Be sure your fingers are not in the way when using the hammer.*

4. Add crushed coal to the massed crucible until it is about one-fourth full.

5. Use the balance to determine the combined mass of the crucible and the crushed coal (fuel). Record this mass in the table.

6. Calculate the mass of the coal by subtracting the mass of the crucible from the combined mass of the crucible and fuel. Record this mass in the table.

Laboratory Activity 1 (continued)

7. Place the crucible containing the crushed coal in the triangle. Light the Bunsen burner and start the timer.

8. As the coal burns, it should give off a red-hot glow. When all the crushed coal is gone and you can no longer see red-hot embers, turn off the Bunsen burner and stop the timer. Record in the table the time it took to completely burn the coal.

9. Allow the crucible to cool for 5 minutes. With the tongs, remove the crucible from the triangle and place it on a hot pad to continue cooling. **WARNING:** *The crucible will still be very hot.*

10. Repeat Steps 2 through 9 using the second crucible and the charcoal briquette.

11. Allow both crucibles to cool completely. Be sure you keep track of which sample is which.

12. Use the balance to determine the mass of each crucible and the residue it contains. Record this mass in the table.

13. Calculate the percentage of residue from each sample by dividing the mass of the residue by the mass of the sample, then multiplying the result by 100.

Data and Observations

	Charcoal	Bituminous Coal
Mass of crucible (g)		
Mass of crucible and fuel (g)		
Mass of fuel (g)		
Mass of crucible and residue after burning (g)		
Mass of residue (g)		
Percentage of residue		
Burning time (min)		

Questions and Conclusions

1. Which sample took longer to burn?

_____

_____

2. Which sample produced the greater percentage of residue?

_____

Laboratory Activity 1 (continued)

3. Which sample—coal or charcoal—was the more efficient fuel? Explain your answer.

_____

_____

_____

4. Predict how you think the efficiency of a sample of anthracite coal would compare to the samples you tested. Explain your answer.

_____

_____

_____

Strategy Check

_____ Can you compare the burning times of charcoal and bituminous coal?

_____ Can you compare the amounts of residue produced from the burning of charcoal and bituminous coal?

_____ Can you infer which fuel is more efficient?

Laboratory Activity

Using Biomass

Chapter 5

Organic materials contain stored energy. When organic materials are used as biomass fuels, the stored energy is released as heat energy. For example, a power plant in Hawaii burns sugarcane waste to produce electricity. In other states, power plants burn wood chips or trash. In this activity, you will compare the amounts of heat given off by burning several examples of biomass.

Strategy

You will compare how biomass fuels burn.
You will compare the amounts of heat produced when different biomass fuels burn.

Materials

30-cm piece of uninsulated, heavy copper wire
test tube
metric ruler
clay
large straight pins (3)
peanut, shelled
water

graduated cylinder
thermometer
aluminum foil
scissors
fireplace matches
mini-marshmallow
half of a wood splint

Procedure

1. Twist the copper wire into a spiral as shown in Figure 1. The top of the spiral should be able to securely hold the test tube.
2. Adjust the height of the spiral so that the bottom of the test tube is about 8 cm above the bottom of the spiral. See Figure 1.
3. Place a small piece of clay in the center of the spiral.
4. Stick the pointed end of a straight pin into a peanut. Stick the other end of the pin into the clay so the pin stands upright, as shown in Figure 2. The bottom of the test tube should not touch the pin.

5. Pour 10 mL of water into the test tube. Place a thermometer in the water and record the water temperature. Record this figure in the Data and Observations section.
6. Wrap the spiral of wire with aluminum foil and cut an opening, as shown in Figure 3.

Figure 2

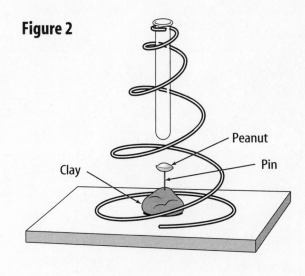

Clay   Peanut   Pin

Figure 1

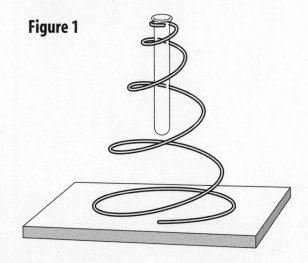

Laboratory Activity 2 (continued)

Figure 3

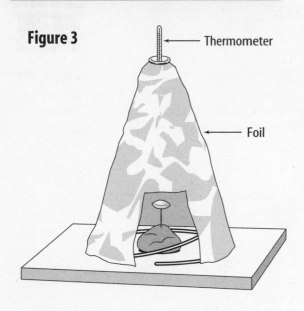

Thermometer

Foil

7. Light the peanut with a match. As the peanut burns, observe any odors or smoke produced. Record your observations in the table.

8. After the peanut is finished burning, measure and record the water temperature. Record the temperature in the table. Observe and describe any residue left behind. Record your observations in the table.

9. Allow the materials to cool for 5 minutes. Then, carefully unwrap the foil covering and remove the pin containing the peanut. Pour out the water in the test tube.

10. Repeat steps 4 through 9 two more times, first using the mini-marshmallow in place of the peanut, then using the piece of wood splint.

Data and Observations

Sample	Start temperature (°C)	Final temperature (°C)	Change in temperature (°C)	Observations
Peanut				
Marshmallow				
Wood splint				

Laboratory Activity 2 (continued)

Questions and Conclusions

1. Did all three samples raise the water temperature an equal amount? Explain.

_____

_____

2. Which sample caused the most smoke? Which caused the least?

_____

_____

_____

3. Did any of the samples cause less odor than the others? Explain.

_____

_____

_____

4. Compare the amounts of residue left after burning the samples.

_____

_____

_____

5. Which sample would you least like to use as a biomass fuel? Explain.

_____

_____

Strategy Check

_____ Can you compare how biomass fuels burn?

_____ Can you compare the amounts of heat given off when different biomass fuels burn?

Determining Latitude

Throughout history people have used the stars to help them keep on course during journeys. In the early days of sailing ships, sailors also used the stars to help them steer a true course. The sailors used a simple instrument called a sextant and the North Star to determine their position. You can also determine your position in degrees of latitude using a simple sextant and the North Star.

Strategy

You will construct a simple sextant.
You will determine your approximate latitude in degrees.

Materials

scissors	nut or metal washer
protractor, Figure 2	thumbtack
glue	tape
cardboard, stiff	plastic straw
string, 20 cm	map of the United States or world atlas

Procedure

1. Cut out the protractor in Figure 2. Glue the protractor to a piece of cardboard. **WARNING:** *Use care when handling sharp objects.*

2. Attach one end of the string to the nut.

3. Attach the free end of the string to the protractor's center hole, using the thumbtack.

4. Tape the plastic straw to the straight edge of the protractor. Your sextant should look like Figure 1.

5. Using a starchart provided by your teacher, locate the North Star. Then sight the North Star through the straw.

6. Looking at the North Star, anchor the string to the sextant using your thumb or fingers. The degree marking on the sextant is the latitude of the North Star. This is your approximate latitude.

7. Record your latitude in Table 1.

8. Repeat steps 5, 6, and 7 three times.

Figure 1

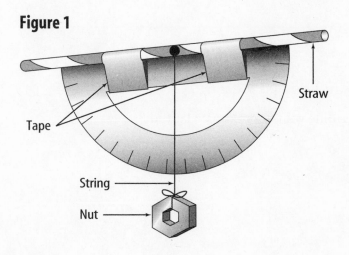

Straw

Tape

String

Nut

Laboratory Activity 1 (continued)

Data and Observations

Table 1

	Latitude (°)
Trial 1	
Trial 2	
Trial 3	
Average	

Questions and Conclusions

1. Calculate the average latitude of your three trials. Show your work.

_____

_____

2. How does your observed latitude compare to the latitude given in the atlas for your location?

_____

_____

3. Explain any differences between your observed latitude and the latitude listed in the atlas.

_____

_____

_____

4. What was the purpose of having three trials and finding an average?

_____

_____

Strategy Check

_____ Can you construct a simple sextant?

_____ Can you determine your approximate latitude?

Laboratory Activity 1 (continued)

Figure 2

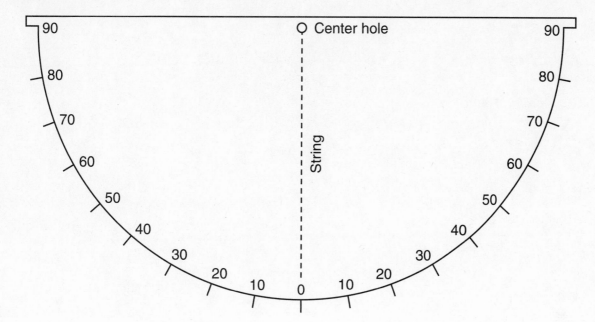

Time Zones

Earth is divided into 24 time zones with 15° of longitude in each zone. Depending on your direction, the time increases or decreases by one hour as you cross each time zone. Directly opposite the prime meridian (0° longitude) is the International Date Line (180° longitude). When you cross the International Date Line, the time increases or decreases by one day. A full day is added when you go west or lost when you go east.

Strategy

You will plan a trip that will take you across several time zones.
You will use distance, speed, and time zones to determine local arrival time.
You will use the International Date Line to determine arrival date.

Materials

meterstick
world map or globe showing longitude and time zones

Procedure

1. You will fly west from Washington, D.C., to Wake Island, part of the Marshall Islands, in the Pacific Ocean. You will depart Washington, D.C., at 8 A.M., Monday, January 1.
2. Locate Washington, D.C., on the world map. Record its longitude below.
3. Locate Wake Island in the Marshall Islands and record its longitude.

4. Measure the map distance between Washington, D.C., and Wake Island in centimeters. Record this measurement and the map scale.
5. Record the number of time zones you cross.
6. Record your direction when you cross the International Date Line.

Data and Observations

1. Washington, D.C. _____ (longitude)

2. Wake Island _____ (longitude)

3. Map scale _____

4. Map distance between Washington, D.C., and Wake Island

_____

5. Number of time zones crossed _____

6. Direction crossing International Date Line _____

Laboratory Activity 2 (continued)

Questions and Conclusions

1. What is the distance, in kilometers, from Washington, D.C., to Wake Island? Show your work.

_____

_____

2. Your plane travels at a speed of 1127 km/h. Calculate the number of hours you will be flying.

_____

_____

3. How many degrees of longitude did you cover in your flight?

_____

4. Calculate the local time of your arrival at Wake Island.

_____

_____

5. If you did not change your watch as you passed through each time zone, what time would your watch read when you arrived at Wake Island?

_____

6. Was your date of arrival different from your date of departure?

_____

7. Did the sun set during your flight? Explain.

_____

_____

_____

Strategy Check

_____ Can you plan a trip that will take you across several time zones?

_____ Can you use distance, speed, and time zones to determine local arrival time?

_____ Can you use the International Date Line to determine arrival date?

Chemical Weathering

LAB 1 Laboratory Activity

Chapter 7

Rocks are mixtures of minerals that are either elements or chemical compounds. Chemical weathering is the chemical reaction of these minerals with carbon dioxide, water, oxygen, or other substances at Earth's surface. For example, in minerals containing iron, the iron reacts with oxygen in the air and moisture to form rust. Rotted plant material combines with water to form humic acids that cause chemical weathering.

Strategy

You will cause a chemical reaction between a copper strip and combined salt and vinegar at room temperature.

You will observe a chemical reaction between iron and atmospheric oxygen and moisture.

Materials

copper strip (dirty)
pie pan (disposable)
graduated cylinder
salt
vinegar (white)
iron (II) sulfate, $FeSO_4$
water
beaker

Procedure

1. For the first activity, place a copper strip in the pie pan and place 5 mL salt on the strip.
2. Carefully pour 30 mL of vinegar over the copper. Record your observations in Table 1.
3. Wash the salt and vinegar off the copper. **WARNING:** *The material formed is an acid. Avoid contact with skin and clothing.*
4. For a separate activity, mix 5 g of iron (II) sulfate in 50 mL of water.

WARNING : *Iron(II) sulfate is poisonous. Avoid contact with skin.* Record the color of the solution and any other observations in Table 1.

5. Let both the beaker and the copper stand undisturbed overnight.
6. Next day, observe the beaker and the copper. Record your observations in Table 1.

Data and Observations

Table 1

	Start	Next day
1. Copper strip		
2. Beaker FeSO₄		

Laboratory Activity 1 (continued)

Questions and Conclusions

1. What happened to the copper when you poured the vinegar over the salt?

_____

_____

2. Is cleaning copper a chemical or physical process? _____

3. Explain what happens to the clean copper left in the air overnight.

_____

_____

4. Why does this reaction follow the cleaning of the copper?

_____

_____

5. Explain what you observed in the beaker of $FeSO_4$.

_____

_____

6. Is this a physical or chemical change? _____

7. Explain the rust-colored stains you see on some rocks. _____

_____

8. How might a soil layer protect rock from chemical weathering?

_____

_____

Strategy Check

_____ Can you observe chemical reactions at Earth's surface?

_____ Can you demonstrate that chemical reactions can occur at room temperature?

Soil Infiltration by Groundwater

Chapter 7

Whether rainwater enters the soil or runs off the surface depends on many factors. One of the most important factors is the type of soil. Also, the rate at which rainwater enters the soil determines whether or not flooding occurs and whether or not septic tanks can be installed safely in a given region. If liquid from the tanks flows outward faster than the soil can absorb it, no filtering action occurs, and sewage reaches the surface and contaminates the area.

This laboratory activity is one of the tests that engineers use to decide if septic tanks are acceptable for a given area. Engineers make the test directly in the ground, sinking the can as far as possible. You may perform the test in the same way, or you may construct a simulated soil sequence and do your testing in the classroom.

Strategy

You will measure the rate at which water filters through soil.

You will plot the rate of infiltration against time.

You will compare various materials to see which are most suitable for filtering groundwater.

Materials

can opener	gravel (500 mL)	water
juice can (large)	slab clay	pointed stick (30 cm long)
cheesecloth (30 cm × 30 cm)	fine sand (500 mL)	pen (felt-tip)
tape (masking)	soil (500 mL)	watch with second hand
dishpan or sink	cardboard (thin)	metric ruler
2 pencils	scissors	graph paper
beaker (500 mL)	plastic bucket	

Procedure

1. With the can opener, cut out both ends of the can. Place the cheesecloth across the bottom of the can and fasten it with tape.

2. Place the can in the dishpan, cloth side down. Raise the can slightly by resting it on the two pencils.

3. Do not fill the can more than half full. Place a layer of gravel in the bottom of the can. Place a layer of clay on the layer of gravel. Place a layer of sand on top of the clay. Place a thick layer of soil on top of the sand.

4. Make a cardboard cover for the can. Cut a small hole (about the diameter of the pointed stick) in the cardboard cover. Cut a small portion from one side of the cover.

Through this hole, you will be able to observe the water level.

5. Fill the rest of the can with water. Place the cover over the top of the can.

6. After about one minute, insert the pointed stick into the can through the small hole until it just touches the top of the water. With the felt-tip pen, draw a line on the stick where it intersects the side of the can.

7. Mark the water depth on the stick every 60 seconds until the soil appears above the water. Determine the various water depths by measuring from the point of the stick to the first mark, second mark, and so on. Record your data in Table 1.

Laboratory Activity 2 (continued)

Data and Observations

Table 1

Time (min)	Water depth (cm)	Time (min)	Water depth (cm)

Graph your data on a sheet of graph paper using the vertical axis for depth of water (cm) and the horizontal axis for time (min).

Questions and Conclusions

1. Is the rate of infiltration constant? Explain.

   _____

   _____

2. Would the rate of infiltration be faster in wet soil or dry soil? Why?

   _____

   _____

3. Which layer infiltrates most slowly? Explain how you got your answer.

   _____

   _____

4. Which layer is most likely to allow the water to move through it too rapidly to be a good filter? Explain how you could design an experiment to find out.

   _____

   _____

Strategy Check

_____ Can you measure the rate at which water filters through soil?

_____ Can you make a graph that shows the rate of infiltration?

_____ Can you compare various materials to see which is suitable for filtering groundwater?

Mass Movements

Chapter 8

The force of gravity causes loose material to move down slope. Sometimes water helps to move the material. Water makes the material heavier and more slippery.

Down slope movements of earth materials may be sudden or slow. Landslides and mudflows are sudden movements. Rocky slopes tend to move as landslides; clay and sand materials may become mudflows.

Creep is an example of slow earth movement. Even when a slope is covered by vegetation, the soil may creep to a lower level.

Strategy

You will cause mass movements.
You will classify the mass movements.

Materials

stream table with hose
4 wood blocks
plastic bucket
protractor
1 L clay
1 L sand
sprinkling can
water
1 L gravel
meterstick

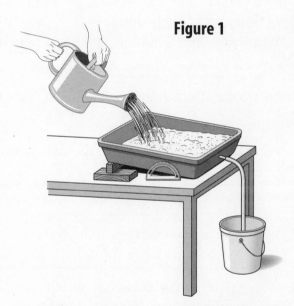

Figure 1

Procedure

1. Set up the stream table as shown in Figure 1.
2. Place the protractor with its flat edge down on the table that is supporting the stream table. Position the protractor next to the lower end of the stream table. Use the protractor to measure the slope angle of the stream table. Record the angle in Table 1.
3. Place the clay in the upper end of the stream table.
4. Pour the sand over the clay. Wet the sand and clay thoroughly until it moves.
5. Observe and record in Table 1 how the mass moves.

6. Add two more blocks under the stream table. Measure and record the new slope angle of the stream table.
7. Move the sand and clay back to the upper end of the stream table.
8. Pour water over the sand and clay until it moves. Record how the mass moves.
9. Remove the sand and clay. Spread a thin layer of clay in the upper end of the table.
10. Spread gravel over the clay. Pour water over the clay and gravel and observe the motion. Record your observations.

Laboratory Activity 1 (continued)

Data and Observations

Table 1

Material	Slope angle (°)	Speed of movement
Sand, clay		
Sand, clay		
Clay, gravel		

Questions and Conclusions

1. What type of mass movement did you cause in steps 3 and 4?

   _____

2. What type of mass movement did you cause in steps 7 and 8?

   _____

3. What caused the difference in speed between these two mass movements?

   _____

   _____

4. What type of mass movement did you cause in steps 9 and 10?

   _____

5. Which type of mass movement would occur during an extended period of heavy rain on a filled area? Explain.

   _____

6. Which type of mass movement, creep or mudflow, is most destructive? Explain.

   _____

   _____

   _____

7. In an area that receives abundant rainfall, how are steep slopes kept from moving downhill?

   _____

Strategy Check

_____ Can you cause mass movements?

_____ Can you classify mass movements?

LAB 2 Laboratory Activity

Modeling a Glacier

Chapter 8

Valley glaciers start in the mountains where snow collects and remains year after year. When the amount of snow accumulation exceeds the amount of snow melting and the snow mass is thick enough, gravity starts the glacier moving downslope. The glacier can take over a river valley as it moves toward a lower elevation. The glacier gouges and scrapes the surface beneath the ice and changes the landscape in many ways.

Strategy

You will construct a model of a valley glacier.
You will show the rugged features a valley glacier forms as it moves and melts.

Materials

cardboard base (21.5 cm × 28 cm)
4 colors of modeling clay
paper for labels
tape (clear)
toothpicks

Procedure

1. On the cardboard base, form a mountain from the darkest piece of clay.
2. Use white clay to show the position of a glacier on your mountain.
3. Show the erosional features of the glacier. Use the toothpicks and paper to make little flags.
4. You might wish to use a thin layer of green clay to show where vegetation has begun to appear.

5. Be sure to model each of the following features: U-shaped valley, cirque, terminal moraine, horn, and outwash plain.
6. Draw a diagram of your model under Data and Observations on the next page. Label the features.

Questions and Conclusions

Write a summary explaining how valley glaciers form and move and how they change the landscape.

_____

_____

_____

_____

_____

Laboratory Activity 2 (continued)

Data and Observations

Draw glacier diagram here.

Strategy Check

_____ Can you construct a model of a valley glacier?

_____ Can you correctly model and label the features left by a valley glacier?

 **Capillary Action**

During a rain, some of the water that moves downward toward the water table and zone of saturation is trapped in tiny, hairlike openings. These openings are called capillaries. Capillaries store molecules of water until a dry period. Then some of the water returns to the surface. Plant roots get moisture from "dry" soil as the moisture moves from saturated soil up the capillaries to the surface.

Strategy

You will demonstrate how moisture moves from saturated soil into the capillaries of dry soil.

Materials

beaker (500-mL)
water
food coloring (red)
celery stalk with leaves
pencils (colored—green, red)

2 plastic drinking glasses (clear)
scissors
0.5 L sand (coarse)
pan

WARNING: *Use care when handling sharp objects.*

Procedure

Part A

1. Fill the beaker half full of water and add a few drops of food coloring. Place the celery in the beaker. In the box labeled "Beginning" under Data and Observations, Part A, draw a diagram of the celery showing the color of the celery.

2. In the box labeled "After 2 days," diagram the celery after two days.

Part B

1. Cut the bottoms from the plastic glasses with scissors. Be careful not to crack the glasses.

2. Set the glasses upright in the pan. Fill each glass with sand.

3. Carefully pour water into one glass until the sand is saturated and some water flows into the pan.

4. Observe and diagram what happens to the water. Draw your diagram under Data and Observations, Part B.

Data and Observations

Part A

Beginning

After 2 Days

Laboratory Activity 1 (continued)

Part B

(blank box)

Questions and Conclusions

1. What happens in the glass of dry sand when the water reaches it?

_____

_____

2. Compare the action of the water in the sand with the action in the celery.

_____

_____

_____

3. How do you know capillary action occurs in the celery?

_____

_____

_____

4. How could capillary action occur in the desert?

_____

_____

_____

5. What kind of rock would be best suited for capillary action?

_____

_____

Strategy Check

_____ Can you demonstrate capillary action in celery?

_____ Can you demonstrate capillary action in soil?

Carbon Dioxide and Limestone

Chapter 9

When carbon dioxide is dissolved in water, it forms a weak acid. This acid dissolves calcite. Many caves have deposits of limestone (calcite) in the form of stalactites and stalagmites. Calcite is also found as the cementing material in many sandstones and other limestones. Thus, limestone can be dissolved beneath the surface, and it can also be deposited beneath the surface.

Strategy

You will examine conditions under which carbon dioxide may be lost from a carbonated soft drink. You will observe the effect of the loss of carbon dioxide on the precipitation of calcium carbonate. You will compare these processes with the natural processes.

Materials

pan
3 cans of carbonated
  soft drinks

ice cubes
hammer
nail

plastic straw (flexible)
limewater ($Ca(OH)_2$ solution)
beaker (100-mL)

Procedure

1. Place one can of carbonated drink in a pan of ice cubes and allow it to cool.
2. When the can is cool, shake it and one of the other cans gently.
3. Remove the top from each of the two cans while holding the cans over the pan or the sink. Record in Table 1 what occurs.
4. With the nail and hammer, make a small hole in the top of the third can. The hole should have about the same diameter as the straw.

5. Carefully slip the straw into the can. Hold the other end in the beaker filled with limewater. **WARNING:** *Limewater may irritate the skin. Avoid contact.* Record your observations in Table 1.

Data and Observations

Table 1

Can	Observations
On ice	
Warm	
Limewater	

Laboratory Activity 2 (continued)

Questions and Conclusions

1. What gas is present in a carbonated drink?

_____

2. What happened when you removed the tops from two of the cans?

_____

Why?

_____

_____

3. Which soft drink lost its carbon dioxide faster?

_____

Why?

_____

_____

4. What process did you observe happening between the soft drink can with the straw and the limewater?

_____

_____

5. As the carbonic acid seeps through the roof of a cave, part of the water evaporates. What happens to the calcium carbonate?

_____

_____

_____

Strategy Check

_____ Can you determine the conditions under which carbon dioxide escapes from a soft drink?

_____ Can you observe the effect of the loss of carbon dioxide on the precipitation of calcium carbonate?

_____ Can you compare the processes observed here with natural processes?

Paleogeographic Mapping

Paleo- means old as in paleontology, the study of old life (fossils). *Geo-* means Earth, as in geology, the study of Earth. *Graphic* refers to a drawing or painting. Therefore, paleogeographic could be translated as "Old Earth Picture." Scientists often use fossil evidence to help them develop a picture of how Earth was long ago. By examining and dating rock formations and fossils of various plants and animals, scientists are able to formulate hypotheses about what Earth's surface might have looked like during a particular period in history. For example, similar rock formations and certain types of plant and animal fossils of a particular age could indicate whether two, now separate, land areas might have been connected during that period. Further analysis of the samples and data could also provide clues to the climate of that area or whether it was dry land or covered by an ocean. To classify events in the geologic past, scientists have divided the millions of years of Earth's history into segments, called *eras*. In this activity, you will examine evidence from the fossil record relative to a current map of an imaginary continent and develop a map of what the continent and the surrounding area might have looked like during the Mesozoic Era (248 million to 65 million years ago).

Strategy

You will determine how fossil evidence can be used to infer information about a continent during the geologic past.

You will interpret fossil evidence to draw a map showing how a continent appeared during the Mesozoic Era.

Materials

colored pencils or markers

Procedure

1. Figure 1 shows a map of a present-day imaginary continent. Locations *A* through *I* are places where fossils have been found in rocks dating to the Mesozoic Era. Study the map and look at the fossils key below the map.

2. From the locations of the different fossils, infer where the land areas were at the time the fossil organisms lived. Keep in mind that the way the modern continent looks may have no relationship to where the land/ocean boundaries were during the Mesozoic Era.

3. Use one color of pencil or marker to color in the land areas on the map in Figure 1. Fill in the block labeled Land with the same color. Use a different color of pencil or marker to color in the ocean areas on the map in Figure 1. Fill in the block labeled Ocean with this color.

4. In the space provided under Data and Observations, draw a map showing land and water areas during the Mesozoic Era. Use the color boundaries you added to Figure 1 as your guideline. Based on these boundaries, add all of the symbols from the map key in Figure 1 to your map.

5. Color all the areas around and between the labeled areas on your map as either land or ocean. Fill in the blocks labeled Land and Ocean with the colors you used.

Laboratory Activity 1 (continued)

Figure 1

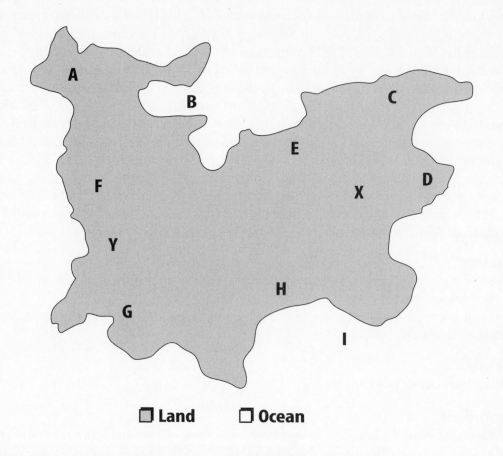

□ **Land**   □ **Ocean**

Fossils found in Mesozoic rocks

A (shark teeth)   F (teeth/bones of small mammals)

B (petrified wood)   G (dinosaur bones)

C (sea stars)   H (corals)

D (leaf and fern imprints)   I (dinosaur footprints)

E (seashell fragments)

X, Y (Areas to be identified after completing your map)

Laboratory Activity 1 (continued)

Data and Observations

Mesozoic Map

☐ **Land**   ☐ **Ocean**

Questions and Conclusions

1. According to your map, was location Y land or water during the Mesozoic Era? Explain how you decided.

_____

_____

2. According to your map, was location X land or water during the Mesozoic Era? Explain how you decided.

_____

3. Compare your map with those of other students. Why do you think that not everyone agreed on whether location X was land or water? How could you find out which interpretation was correct?

_____

_____

_____

Laboratory Activity 1 (continued)

4. Corals grow only in warm, shallow oceans near the coastlines of continents that are relatively near the equator. Would knowing this fact make you revise your map? Why or why not?

_____

_____

_____

5. Suppose the modern continent shown in Figure 1 was located in an area that is extremely cold. Using the evidence you have, plus the information in Question 4, what could you infer about the continent?

_____

_____

_____

Strategy Check

_____ Can you determine how fossil evidence can be used to infer information about a continent during the geologic past?

_____ Can you interpret fossil evidence to draw a map showing how a continent appeared during the Mesozoic Era?

How do continental plates move?

One of the models that helps explain how tectonic plates move is the convection model. In this hypothesis, the molten magma of the mantle boils like water in a pot. The pattern of the moving water forms a circular wave or current as hot water rises to the top and cooler surface water is forced to the side of the pot and back down to be heated again. Inside the Earth it is believed there are many convection cells, or regions in the mantle, that boil like this. The different cells have their own currents and constantly move independently of one another. The crust of the Earth has a much lighter mass and density than the magma. As a result, the plates of crust are moved by convection currents and broken up on the boiling surface of the mantle.

Strategy

You will model convection currents and the movement of tectonic plates.
You will predict what will happen to tectonic plates at the margins of convection cells.

Materials

hot plate   scissors   tongs
water   medium to large–mouthed pot
sheets of plastic foam wrap for padding packages (not made from corn or organic materials)

Procedure

1. The hot plates should be turned on high. Carefully fill the pot 2/3 full of water and place it on the hot plate. It will take a while for the water to boil.

2. Obtain a piece of flat plastic foam wrap. Use scissors to cut several shapes that represent tectonic plates. If you are working in a group you may mark your tectonic plates with a pencil or pen if you wish so that you can recognize it when the water boils.

3. Carefully place your pieces of foam on the surface of the water. If the water has any steam or tiny bubbles at the bottom of the pan, ask your teacher to place the foam in the pot for you.

4. As the water heats, watch the action of the bubbles as they rise from the bottom of the pot. Observe everything you can about what happens to them when they rise under a piece of foam. Record your observation in the table provided.

5. Once the water begins to boil, watch your pieces of foam. How do they move? In what direction do they go? Do they stay in one place in the pot or do they move ? Do they crash into other pieces of foam?

Record the answers to these observations in the data table. Be sure to observe the boiling pot for a while. It may first seem there is no pattern to the action in the pot, but careful observation will reveal certain movements in the boiling water.

Figure 1

Foam

Laboratory Activity 2 (continued)

6. When the experiment is over, your teacher will turn off the hot plates and remove the foam with tongs for cooling. DO NOT remove the pieces yourself. They will cool quickly. When they are cooled, find your pieces and return to your lab station or seat.

7. In your data table write down any observed changes in your foam. Does it still have water in it? Have any of the corners been melted or damaged? Write down any other observations in your table.

Data and Observations

Action of bubbles	1.
Movement of foam pieces in boiling water	2.
Condition of foam after experiment	3.

Questions and Conclusions

1. How did you describe what happened to the bubbles as they gathered under the foam? What happened at the sides of the foam?

_____

_____

_____

Laboratory Activity 2 (continued)

2. What type of natural feature is similar to the action of the bubbles? Explain your answer.

_____

_____

_____

3. Describe the movement of the plastic pieces when the water started to boil. Could you see a pattern?

_____

_____

_____

4. How does this experiment model the moving tectonic plates?

_____

_____

5. How is this experiment different from the real world in terms of tectonic plates? (Hint: What were your foam pieces like after the experiment?)

_____

_____

_____

6. Predict what would happen if the convection currents of the molten magma changed direction or stopped altogether?

_____

_____

_____

Strategy Check

_____ Can you model convection currents and the movement of tectonic plates?

_____ Can you predict what will happen to tectonic plates at the margins of convection cells?

Using the Modified Mercalli Scale to Locate an Epicenter

Earthquakes are classified using different scales. The Richter scale is a measure of the energy released during the earthquake. The Modified Mercalli scale is a measure of the amount of damage done by the earthquake. Scientists record responses from many people who experience the earthquake and assign a value from I (1) to XII (12). These numbers are plotted on a map and used to locate the epicenter of the earthquake. This method is based on the idea that the area closest to the epicenter will suffer the most damage.

Strategy

You will read simulated reports of people's earthquake experiences and then assign Modified Mercalli scale values to these reports.

You will plot these values on a map and locate the epicenter of the earthquake.

Materials

colored pencils

Procedure

1. Read the Modified Mercalli scale in Table 1 so you become familiar with the descriptions.
2. Read the list of experiences from the various cities in Table 2. Assign a Mercalli value to each of the descriptions. Then write each value on the map (Figure 1) next to the corresponding city.
3. Use colored pencils to draw lines that connect cities having the same Mercalli value.
4. Use the pattern you have drawn to estimate where the epicenter is located.

Laboratory Activity 1 (continued)

Data and Observations

Table 1

		Modified Mercalli Scale
I.	(1)	Earth movement is not felt by people.
II.	(2)	A few people may feel movement if they are sitting still. Hanging objects may sway.
III.	(3)	Felt noticeably indoors, especially on upper floors. May not be recognized as an earthquake.
IV.	(4)	During the day, felt indoors by many people, outdoors by few. At night, some are awakened. Dishes, windows, and doors rattle.
V.	(5)	Felt by almost everyone. Sleeping people are awakened. Some windows are broken and plaster cracked. Some unstable objects are overturned. Bells ring.
VI.	(6)	Felt by everyone. Many people are frightened and run outdoors. Some heavy furniture is moved, and some plaster may fall. Overall damage is slight.
VII.	(7)	People run outdoors. Earth movement is noticed by people driving cars. Damage is slight in well-built buildings and considerable in poorly built structures. Some chimneys are broken.
VIII.	(8)	Damage is slight in well-designed buildings and extreme in poorly built structures. Chimneys and walls may fall.
IX.	(9)	Damage is considerable in well-designed buildings. Buildings shift from their foundations and partly collapse. Ground may crack, and underground pipes are broken.
X.	(10)	Some well-built wooden structures are destroyed. Most masonry structures destroyed. Ground is badly cracked.
XI.	(11)	Few, if any, structures remain standing. Broad open cracks in the ground.
XII.	(12)	Complete destruction. Waves are seen on the ground surface.

Laboratory Activity 1 (continued)

Table 2

		Earthquake Observations and Data
1.	Ashland	Hanging lamps swayed.
2.	Bear Creek	People outdoors did not notice anything, but windows and doors rattled.
3.	Burneville	Felt by people sitting at dinner.
4.	Cedar Pass	Families sitting at dinner noticed the dishes rattling.
5.	Dodge	Dishes, windows, and doors rattled.
6.	Emeryville	Not felt.
7.	Falls	Felt by nearly everybody. A few windows were broken.
8.	Forks	Big windows in stores downtown were broken.
9.	Grants Plain	Church bells rang all over town. Plaster walls developed cracks. Candlesticks fell off the mantel.
10.	Greenburg	Not much damage but felt by everyone.
11.	Hillsdale	Some plaster ceilings fell. Many people were scared.
12.	Kempoe	Felt by some people on upper floors. Some windows rattled.
13.	Leeds	Noticed by many people working late in tall buildings.
14.	Oakdale	Felt by a few people.
15.	Peterson	Felt by almost everyone. Some plaster ceilings fell down.
16.	Red Hills	Some people are awakened out of their sleep.
17.	River Glen	Felt by almost everybody in town.
18.	Sandpoint	Many windows were broken. Some people were scared.
19.	Split Rock	Poorly built structures were badly damaged. A few drivers noticed their cars moving strangely for a moment.
20.	Travis City	Almost everyone felt it. Church bells rang.
21.	Tucker	Books fell off the shelves in the main library, and some windows were broken.
22.	Vernon	Dishes in the cupboard rattled. Felt by people indoors.
23.	Victor	Most people were alarmed and ran outside. Chimneys were broken.
24.	Vista	Felt by people in upper floors of tall buildings.
25.	Wells	Noticed by people on the third floor. Some windows rattled.
26.	Westbury	Some people noticed the vibration but thought it was a freight train.
27.	Wheatfield	People sitting at the dinner table noticed doors and windows rattling.
28.	Yalco	Many people ran outside. Many windows were broken.

Laboratory Activity 1 (continued)

Figure 1

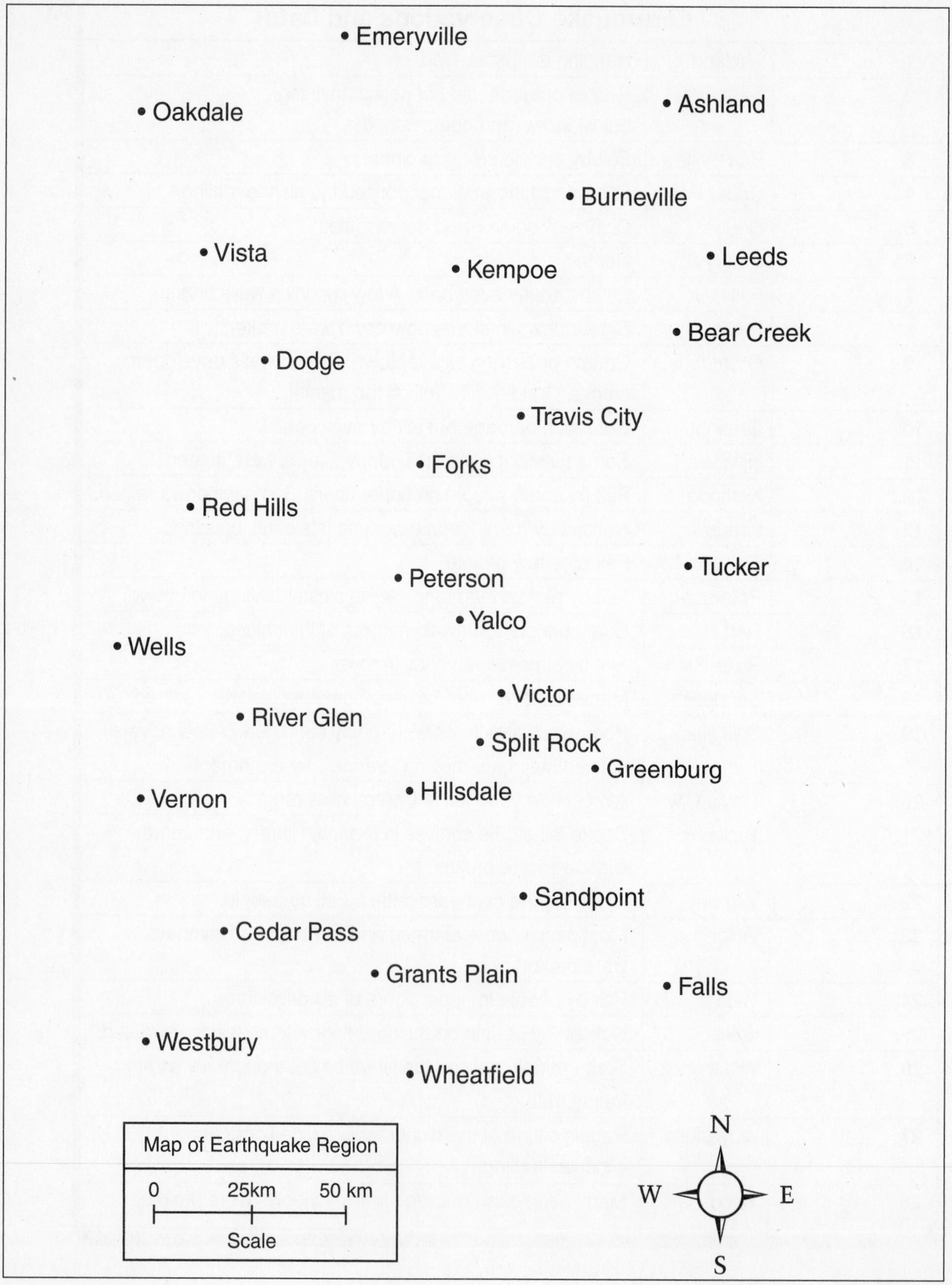

Map of Earthquake Region

0   25km   50 km

Scale

Laboratory Activity 1 (continued)

Questions and Conclusions

1. What cities were closest to the epicenter of the earthquake? How did you determine this?

   _____

   _____

2. Approximately how wide was the zone with a rating of V or higher?

   _____

3. What are some possible sources of error when using the Modified Mercalli scale to locate the epicenter of an earthquake?

   _____

   _____

   _____

   _____

Strategy Check

_____ Can you determine Mercalli values?

_____ Can you locate earthquake epicenters?

LAB 2 Laboratory Activity

Earthquakes

Seismologists—the scientists who study earthquakes—have found that certain areas are more likely to have earthquakes than others. The risk is greater in these areas because they lie over active geologic faults. Maps that pinpoint earthquakes all over the world show that the greatest seismic belt borders the Pacific Ocean. Every state in the United States has had at least one earthquake, but some states have had stronger and more frequent earthquakes than others.

A magnitude-5 earthquake is classified as moderate, a magnitude-6 earthquake is large, and a magnitude-7 earthquake is major. An earthquake with a magnitude of 8 or larger is classified as great.

Strategy

You will study the occurrence of strong earthquakes in the United States by plotting earthquakes on a map.

You will determine which areas of the United States are most likely to have strong earthquakes.

Procedure

1. Plot the data from Table 1 in the Data and Observations section on Map 1. Place one dot in the state for each recorded earthquake. Use an atlas or other reference to help you locate the states.
2. Count the number of dots within each state and write that number within the state's borders.

Data and Observations

Table 1

Some Earthquakes in the United States with a Magnitude of 7 and Above					
State	**Year**	**Magnitude**	**State**	**Year**	**Magnitude**
Alaska	1964	9.2	California	1872	7.8
Alaska	1957	8.8	California	1892	7.8
Alaska	1965	8.7	Missouri	1811	7.7
Alaska	1938	8.3	California	1906	7.7
Alaska	1958	8.3	Nevada	1915	7.7
Alaska	1899	8.2	Missouri	1812	7.6
Alaska	1899	8.2	California	1992	7.6
Alaska	1986	8.0	California	1952	7.5
Missouri	1812	7.9	California	1927	7.3
California	1857	7.9	Nevada	1954	7.3
Hawaii	1868	7.9	Montana	1959	7.3
Alaska	1900	7.9	Idaho	1983	7.3
Alaska	1987	7.9	California	1922	7.3

Laboratory Activity 2 (continued)

Questions and Conclusions

1. In what regions have damaging earthquakes been concentrated?

   _____

   _____

   _____

2. From the table, which earthquake(s) can be classified as great?

   _____

   _____

   _____

   _____

3. What does a concentration of damaging earthquakes indicate about the underlying rock structure of the area?

   _____

   _____

   _____

   _____

4. Can you be sure that an earthquake could not occur in any area?

   _____

   _____

5. According to the map, is it likely that a damaging earthquake will occur in your state?

   _____

6. The earthquakes in 1811 and 1812 in Missouri occurred near the Mississippi River. The soil near the river tends to be wet. Do you think liquefaction took place during the earthquakes? Why or why not?

   _____

   _____

   _____

   _____

Strategy Check

_____ Can you observe where most damaging earthquakes have occurred in the United States?

_____ Can you predict the parts of the United States most likely to experience strong earthquakes?

Laboratory Activity 2 (continued)

Map 1

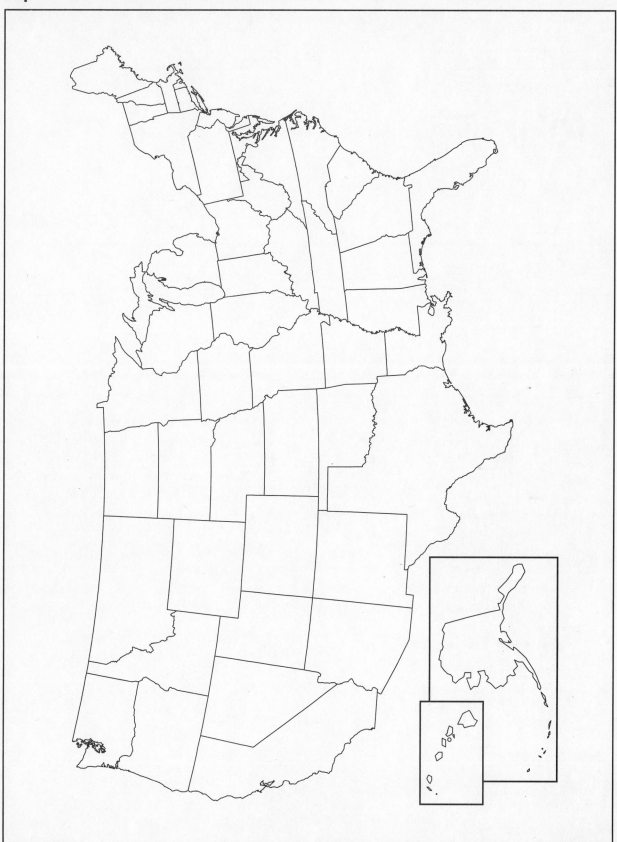

Volcanic Preservation

On May 18, 1980, Mount St. Helens in Washington erupted for the first time in 123 years. Volcanologists, people who study volcanoes, estimated that Mount St. Helens spewed enough rock and ash to cover an area of 2.6 km² to a depth of 172.8 m. This amount of ash is almost as much as Mt. Vesuvius poured onto Pompeii in 79 A.D. Organisms rapidly buried by the ash from volcanic eruptions may be preserved as fossils. Many examples were found in the excavation of Pompeii.

Strategy
You will form a "fossil" by drying.
You will compare the fossil to a living sample.

Materials 🥽 🧤
brush (soft)
silica powder or borax
cake tin with lid
flowers (several different kinds)
pencils (colored)
metric ruler

Procedure
1. Draw each flower specimen and record its properties in Table 1.
2. Pour silica powder into the tin to a depth of 5 cm.
3. Arrange fresh flowers on the silica powder. Carefully sprinkle silica powder over the flowers to a depth of 5 to 8 cm.
4. Put the lid on the tin and allow the tin to stand undisturbed for three weeks.
5. Carefully pour off the silica powder and examine the flowers.
6. Compare the appearance of the dried flowers to that of the fresh specimens.

Data and Observations

Table 1

Property	Fresh	Dried
Color		
Size		
Other		

Laboratory Activity 1 (continued)

Questions and Conclusions

1. How does the appearance of the dried flowers compare to that of the fresh flowers?

_____

_____

2. What was the purpose in using silica powder?

_____

_____

3. How is silica powder like volcanic ash?

_____

_____

4. What other natural agent might preserve fossils in the same way as volcanic ash?

_____

_____

5. Is your dried flower a true fossil? What else would have to happen to it?

_____

_____

Strategy Check

_____ Can you form a "fossil" by drying?

_____ Can you compare this fossil to a living sample?

Volcanic Eruptions

Some volcanic eruptions consist of violent explosions of gases and tephra, while others involve a relatively quiet flow of lava around a vent. The type of eruption that occurs depends on both the composition of the magma and the amount of gas trapped in it. Thick magma that is rich in silica tends to trap steam and other gases. The more gas in the magma, the greater the pressure that builds up in the volcano. The tremendous pressure that builds in silica-rich magma is released when the volcano erupts explosively.

By contrast, magma that contains less silica tends to be less explosive and flow more easily. This type of magma is rich in iron and magnesium and traps smaller amounts of gas. It produces basaltic lava that flows from a volcano in broad, flat layers. In this lab, you will model both basaltic lava flows and explosive eruptions.

Strategy

You will model and observe how the buildup of pressure in a volcano can lead to an explosive eruption.

You will determine how layers of basaltic lava accumulate.

Materials 🥽 🧤

newspaper
balloons (9)
empty coffee can
measuring cup
plaster of paris
water
1 lb. plastic margarine tubs (2)
red, blue, and green food coloring
wooden paint stirrers (3)

old paintbrushes (3)
sponge
marker
meterstick
scissors
piece of thick cardboard (approximately 50 cm × 50 cm)
textbooks
small tubes of toothpaste in different colors
   (white, green, striped)

CAUTION: *Never put anything you use in a laboratory experiment into your mouth.*

Procedure

Part A—Modeling Explosive Eruptions

1. Work in a group of five or six students. Put on your apron and goggles, and cover your work area with sheets of newspaper.

2. Inflate six of the balloons. Put less air in some of the balloons than in others. You'll need two small balloons, two medium, and two large. Leave the remaining balloons uninflated.

3. In the coffee can, combine 1 L of plaster mix with 2 L of water. Stir the mixture with a wooden stirrer until the mixture is smooth. You should use a bit more water than the directions on the box suggest. Thinner plaster will be easier to work with.

4. Pour about one-third of the mixture into each of the plastic tubs, leaving the final third in the can. Add several drops of food coloring to each container, and stir.

You should end up with three colors of plaster: red, green, and blue. Do this step as quickly as possible since the plaster mix will begin to harden.

5. Using paintbrushes, coat the entire surface of each of the inflated balloons with a thin layer of plaster. Paint the two small balloons blue, the medium balloons green, and the large balloons red. Using any color, paint a band around the center of each of the empty balloons, leaving the ends unpainted (Figure 1). Set the balloons on sheets of newspaper to dry. If you spill any plaster while you are painting, wipe it up with a damp sponge.

Laboratory Activity 2 (continued)

Figure 1

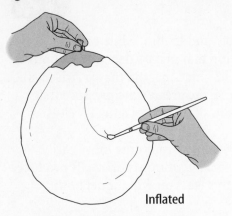

Inflated

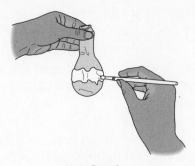

Uninflated

6. While the plaster is drying, skip to Part B of the procedure.

7. To model the buildup of pressure inside magma, try to inflate the empty balloons. What do you observe? Record your observation in the Data and Observations section.

8. Spread newspapers on an open area of the floor. With the marker, draw a large X on the center of the paper. To model an explosive eruption, take one of the small, blue balloons and place it on the X. Pop the balloon by stepping on it. Leave the pieces of the plaster in place and pop the second small balloon in the same way. **CAUTION:** *Wear your safety goggles throughout this experiment.*

9. With the meterstick, measure the distance from the X to the piece of plaster that landed the farthest from it. This distance represents the radius of the debris field. Record this measurement in Table 1 the Data and Observations section.

10. Repeat step 8 using the medium balloons. Measure and record the distance from the X to the piece of *green* plaster that landed farthest from it.

11. Repeat step 8 using the large balloons. Measure and record the distance from the X to the piece of *red* plaster that landed farthest from it.

Part B—Modeling Basaltic Lava Flows

1. Use the scissors to poke a hole near the center of the piece of cardboard. Widen the hole until it is just large enough for the cap of a tube of toothpaste to fit through it.

2. Make two stacks of books and place the cardboard on top of them so that the hole is suspended about 30 cm above your work surface (Figure 2).

3. Remove the cap from one of the tubes of toothpaste. Stick the cap end of the tube through the hole so that the tube is upright and just the mouth is sticking out the top of the cardboard. Model a basaltic lava flow by slowly squeezing out the contents of the tube.

4. Measure the height and diameter of your "lava" flow and record your measurements in Table 2 in the Data and Observations section.

5. To model additional eruptions, repeat steps 3 and 4 using the other two tubes of toothpaste to add to your "lava" flow.

6. Return to step 7 of Part A.

Figure 2

Laboratory Activity 2 (continued)

Data and Observations

What did you observe when you inflated the plaster-coated balloons?

_____

Table 1

Balloon size	Radius of debris field (cm)
Small 1	
Small 2	
Medium 1	
Medium 2	
Large 1	
Large 2	

Table 2

Eruption	Diameter (cm)	Height (cm)
1		
2		
3		

Questions and Conclusions

1. The air in your balloons modeled the gases that build up in silica-rich magma. Which balloons (small, medium, or large) modeled magma under the greatest pressure? Explain.

_____

_____

2. What do your results from Part A tell you about the relationship between pressure and the force of an explosive volcanic eruption?

_____

_____

3. What type or types of volcano did you model in Part A? Explain your answer.

_____

_____

Laboratory Activity 2 (continued)

4. What were you modeling when you inflated the plaster-coated balloons in step 7 of Part A?

_____

_____

5. a. In Part B, how did the layers of toothpaste accumulate? Did the second and third layers form on top of the first layer or beneath it?

_____

_____

   b. What does this result tell you about the age of the top layer of basaltic lava on a volcano compared with lower layers?

_____

_____

6. How did the height of the volcano you modeled in Part B compare with its width? What type of volcano has this shape?

_____

_____

7. How did the two types of eruptions you modeled differ from one another? How were they alike?

_____

_____

_____

Strategy Check

_____ Can you model an explosive eruption due to the buildup of gas pressure?

_____ Can you describe how layers of basaltic lava accumulate?

Principle of Superposition

The principle of superposition states that beds in a series are laid down with the oldest at the bottom and successively younger layers on top. Beds may be exposed at the surface as a result of folding and uplifting or because of faulting. If part, or all, of a layer is removed by erosion and this surface is covered by a new deposit, the contact is called an unconformity. In some areas, river erosion will cut deeply enough to expose a number of layers, such as in the Grand Canyon.

Strategy

You will construct a map legend.
You will construct a block diagram of an area.
You will write the geologic history of the area.

Materials

block diagram, Figure 1
glue or paste
cardboard, thin
pencils (colored)
scissors
tape (clear)

Procedure

1. Set up a legend for your diagram and select a color for each layer. Record the legend in Table 1.
2. Glue Figure 1 on the cardboard. Color the map according to your legend.
3. Cut out, fold, and tape the block diagram as instructed on Figure 1.

Data and Observations

Table 1

	Color
Layer A	
Layer B	
Layer C	
Layer D	

Questions and Conclusions

1. Which layer is oldest? Explain.

_____

_____

_____

2. What kind of structure do the layers have?

_____

_____

_____

Laboratory Activity 1 (continued)

3. Why is the glacial till not folded?

_____

_____

_____

4. What does the presence of the peat and soil layer in the glacial till tell you?

_____

_____

_____

5. Was this a mountainous area prior to glaciation? Explain.

_____

_____

_____

_____

_____

6. How many advances of the ice occurred here?

_____

7. Write the geologic history of the area illustrated in the block diagram.

_____

_____

_____

_____

_____

_____

_____

Strategy Check

_____ Can you set up a map legend?

_____ Can you construct a block diagram?

_____ Can you write the geologic history of the area illustrated by a block diagram?

Laboratory Activity 1 (continued)

Figure 1

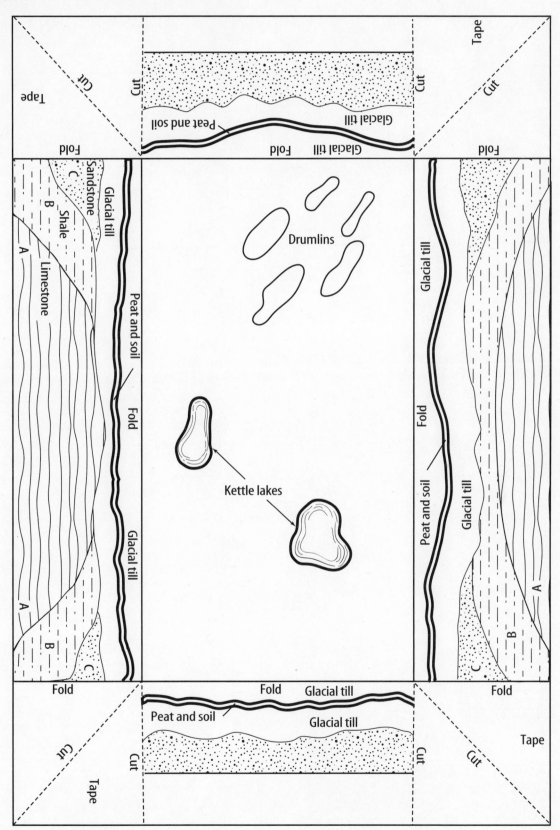

Index Fossils

Fossils found in the deepest layer of undisturbed rocks in an area represent the oldest forms of life in that particular rock formation. When reading Earth history, these layers would be "read" from bottom to top, or oldest to most recent. If a specific fossil is typically found only in a particular type of rock and is found in many places worldwide, the fossil might be useful as index fossil. The index fossil can be useful in determining the age of layers of rock or soil. By comparing this type of information from rock formations in various parts of the world, scientists have been able to establish the geologic time scale.

Strategy

You will make trace fossils from several objects.
You will distinguish between index fossils and other fossils.

Materials 🥽 🔨 ✋ 💧

newspaper
objects to use in making trace fossils (3)
clay
container, at least 25 cm × 20 cm × 15 cm (or approximately shoe-box size)
varieties of "soil" (3)
*sand
*potting soil
*pea gravel
*mulch
*shredded dried leaves
*fresh grass cuttings
small shovel
*scoop
*Alternate materials

Procedure

1. Cover your desk or table with several layers of newspaper. Select three objects to use to make your trace fossils. Label these objects A, B, and C.

2. Make trace fossils of the three objects by pressing clay onto each of them. Carefully remove the clay from the objects. Label your trace fossils A, B, and C, and set your fossils aside. Make a second trace fossil from objects A and C. Label these.

3. Choose three different types of soil. You can have different amounts of each type of soil, but together the three soils should almost fill your container.

4. Layer one type of soil into your container. Bury one trace fossil A in this layer of soil. Sketch this layer in Figure 1 in the Data and Observations section. Be sure to note the location of the fossil.

5. Repeat step 4 twice using a different type of soil for each layer. In the second layer, bury trace fossils A, B, and C. Place only trace fossil C in the third layer. Fossil B is your index fossil.

Laboratory Activity 2 (continued)

6. Choose a time period that each of your soil layers represents, and add this information to Figure 1. Consider the distribution of fossils in the layers of soil when you select the time span for each object. Also, because fossil B is your index fossil, it must represent a unique time period. Be sure that the time period you select for the middle layer does not overlap with the other time spans.

7. Exchange containers with another group. Tell the group when object B, your index fossil, existed.

8. Carefully excavate your new container. Sketch each layer in Figure 2 as you proceed with the excavation. Carefully note where each fossil is found. Compare your sketches with the sketches made by the group who made the container.

9. Based on the age of the index fossil, determine what you can know about a time line for the second container. Add details on what you can tell about the time line to Figure 2.

Data and Observations

Figure 1—First Container

Layer	Bottom	Middle	Top
Time period			
Sketch			

Figure 2—Excavated Container

Layer	Bottom	Middle	Top
Time period			
Sketch			

Laboratory Activity 2 (continued)

Questions and Conclusions

1. Explain why an index fossil must represent a unique time period.

   _____

   _____

2. Are the three fossils in the middle layer from the same time period?

   _____

   _____

3. Is fossil A in the deepest layer from the same type of organism as fossil A in the middle layer?

   _____

   _____

4. Are the two fossils from object A from the same time period? What do you know about the duration of organism A in the geologic time line?

   _____

   _____

5. What is important to note while you are excavating?

   _____

   _____

6. Compare your sketch of the container you excavated with the sketch made by the makers of that container? Explain any important differences.

   _____

   _____

7. Explain how an index fossil is used to determine the age of surrounding fossils.

   _____

   _____

   _____

   _____

Strategy Check

_____ Can you make trace fossils from a variety of objects?

_____ Can you determine the index fossil in the excavation?

Differences in a Species

To use fossil dating efficiently, paleontologists first separate fossils into groups. The most useful group for classification is called a species. A species is a population of individuals that have similar characteristics. Small differences in individuals might result in the development of a new species by a series of gradual changes. These changes can be traced from one geologic time division to another if the fossil record is good.

Strategy

You will describe the variations present within a species.
You will describe a species in terms of one characteristic.

Materials

meterstick   graph paper   pencils (colored)

Procedure

1. The species you will study is *Homo sapiens,* or yourself. You and your classmates are all members of this species. Remember that all living things grow at different rates. It is possible that you will find some big differences in your study, but everyone still belongs to the same species.

2. Record all characteristics of the species that you can. Record which of the characteristics you could measure and compare for all members of the species.

3. Measure and record in Table 1 the height of yourself and each of your classmates. Round off the height to the nearest tenth of a meter (0.1 m).

4. Measure the heights of a class of younger students. Record this data in Table 2.

Data and Observations

1. Characteristics: _____

_____

Table 1

Name	Height (m)	Name	Height (m)	Name	Height (m)

Laboratory Activity 1 (continued)

Table 2

Name	Height (m)	Name	Height (m)	Name	Height (m)

Use a separate sheet of paper to graph the Frequency (number of persons having the same height) on the vertical axis against the Height (m) on the horizontal axis. Use one color for your own class and a second color for the younger class.

Questions and Conclusions

1. On what characteristics can you classify this group as a single species?

_____

2. Where do most of the members of your class fall in regard to height?

_____

3. Where do most of the members of the younger class fall in regard to height?

_____

4. What change has taken place over time?

_____

5. How is this activity like fossil dating?

_____

_____

6. How is this activity different from fossil dating? (Hint: Think in terms of the time spans involved.)

_____

_____

Strategy Check

_____ Can you describe the variations present within a species?

_____ Can you describe a species in terms of a range of a characteristic?

LAB 2 Laboratory Activity

Looking at the Geologic Time Scale

Chapter 14

As you have learned, Earth's history can be divided in geologic time segments called eras, periods, and epochs. These time periods are useful for placing events such as the disappearance of the dinosaurs and the appearance of humans in perspective relative to the history of life on Earth. The time segments are not as equal as they sound, however. In earlier eras, life processes on Earth appear to have been developing quite slowly, whereas later eras saw enormous changes over relatively short segments of geologic time. In this Laboratory Activity you will compare and contrast various segments of Earth's history by constructing a geologic time line.

Strategy

You will make a graph to compare the durations of Earth's geologic eras.

You will measure and construct a time line that shows Earth's geologic eras.

You will identify time relationships among events in Earth's geologic history.

You will record and illustrate significant events during the Mesozoic and Cenozoic Eras on a time line.

Materials

4–4.5 m of adding machine tape
meter stick
colored pencils

Procedure

Part A

1. Figure 1 shows approximately how long ago each major division of Earth's geologic time scale began. Use the information to calculate how long each of these divisions lasted. Record that information in the last column of Figure 1.

2. Using that information, make a bar graph on the grid in the Data and Observations section to show how long each division lasted.

Part B

3. You will use a piece of adding machine tape to make a geologic time line. Distance will represent time, with 1 cm representing 10 million years.

4. Using the meter stick, draw a straight line through the middle of the tape from one end to the other.

5. Starting at the left end of the tape, measure a distance that represents the length of Precambrian Time. Refer back to the time duration you calculated in Figure 1. Make a vertical line at the correct point.

To the left of that line label the division on your time line *Precambrian Time*.

6. From that vertical line, measure a distance that represents the length of the Paleozoic Era. Refer back to the time duration you calculated in Figure 1. Make a vertical line at the correct point. To the left of that line, label the division on your time line *Paleozoic Era*.

7. Repeat step 6 for the Mesozoic Era and the Cenozoic Era.

8. Lightly color each division on your time line a different color.

9. Divide the Mesozoic Era and the Cenozoic Era into the Periods and Epochs shown in Figure 2.

10. Then, using information from your text (such as the mass extinction) and the additional information in Figure 2, mark in the correct positions on your time line for significant events that occurred during the Mesozoic and Paleozoic Eras. Illustrate each of these events with a small drawing.

Laboratory Activity 2 (continued)

Data and Observations

Figure 1

Major geologic time division	When time division began	Length of time division lasted
Precambrian time	4.0 billion years ago	
Paleozoic era	544 million years ago	
Mesozoic era	245 million years ago	
Cenozoic era	65 million years ago	

Figure 2

Division	Time period (millions of years ago)	Event(s)
Triassic period	248–213	breakup of Pangaea
Jurassic period	213–145	first birds
Cretaceous period	145–65	Rocky Mountains form; first flowering plants
Paleocene epoch	65–55.5	first hooved mammals
Eocene epoch	55.5–33.7	first whales
Oligocene epoch	33.7–23.8	early formation of European Alps
Miocene epoch	23.8–5.3	first dogs and bears
Pliocene epoch	5.3–1.8	first Ice Age; first hominoids
Pleistocene epoch	1.8–0.008	modern humans
Holocene epoch	0.0008–present	Sea levels rose as climate warmed; first civilizations

Laboratory Activity 2 (continued)

Graph

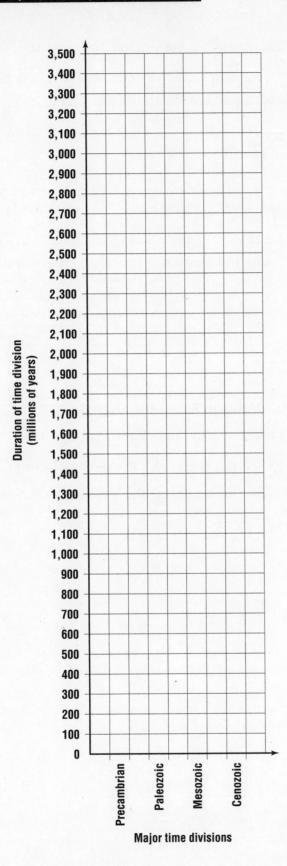

Laboratory Activity 2 (continued)

Questions and Conclusions

1. Based on your graph in Part A, which time division is the longest? The shortest?

_____

2. About how many times longer than the Mesozoic Era was the Paleozoic Era?

_____

3. In which era do you live today? In which epoch?

_____

4. About how many times longer than modern humans have hooved mammals lived on Earth?

_____

5. What problems did you have in constructing and illustrating your time line? Why did you have those problems?

_____

_____

Strategy Check

_____ Can you make a graph to compare the durations of Earth's geologic eras?

_____ Can you measure and construct a time line that shows Earth's geologic eras?

_____ Can you identify time relationships among events in Earth's geologic history?

_____ Can you record and illustrate significant events during the Mesozoic and Cenozoic Eras on a time line?

Air Volume and Pressure

You can't always see the air in Earth's atmosphere, but air is real. Like any other form of matter, air has definite physical properties. As you work through this activity, you will observe two of the properties of air—volume and pressure.

Strategy

You will demonstrate that air has volume (occupies space).
You will demonstrate that air exerts pressure.

Materials

water
beaker (500-ml)

bicycle pump
air mattress

meterstick

Procedure

1. Put 250 ml of water in the beaker.
2. Insert the hose of the bicycle pump so it is below the surface of the water.
3. To demonstrate that air occupies space, pump air into the water. Record your observations. Remove the pump hose.
4. To demonstrate that air exerts pressure, place the air mattress on the floor. Press the mattress flat to be sure it contains very little air. Feel the floor through the mattress.

5. Measure in centimeters the length, width, and thickness of the air mattress. Record your measurements in Table 1.
6. Inflate the mattress using the bicycle pump. Measure and record the dimensions of the mattress again.
7. Push down with your hand on one area of the inflated air mattress. Note how the dimensions of the area you are pushing on change. How does the part of the mattress surrounding your hands change?

Data and Observations

Observations:

1. Air pumped into beaker:

_____

_____

2. Pushing down on mattress:

_____

_____

Table 1

Air mattress	Before pumping	After pumping
1. Length (cm)		
2. Width (cm)		
3. Thickness (cm)		

Laboratory Activity 1 (continued)

Questions and Conclusions

1. What happened in the beaker of water when you pumped air into it?

_____

_____

2. What property of air does this demonstrate?

_____

_____

3. Calculate the volume of air in the air mattress. Show your work below. If you need more room, use the back of this page.

4. What happened to the thickness of the air mattress in the area where you pushed on it?

_____

5. What happened to the area of the air mattress surrounding the area you pushed? What property of air does this show?

_____

_____

6. Does air exert pressure? Defend your answer.

_____

_____

_____

_____

Strategy Check

_____ Can you demonstrate that air has volume?

_____ Can you demonstrate that air exerts pressure?

LAB 2 Laboratory Activity

Temperature of the Air

Air temperature is an important factor in the scientific study of weather. Air temperature affects air pressure and, thus, the type of weather that may occur. Differences in air temperature also cause winds. By studying the air temperature and weather at different times during the day, you may be able to predict how the air temperature will affect local weather.

Strategy

You will measure air temperature at different times during the day.

You will measure air temperature at the same location each time.

You will graph your results and compare your graph with those of your classmates.

Materials

Celsius thermometer (metal backed)

graph paper

Procedure

1. Select an outdoor site for taking air temperature readings. Make sure the site is an open shaded area.

2. Record the air temperature at this site three times each day for a week. Be careful to read the thermometer at the same times each day. Record data in Table 1.

3. Record additional weather factors, such as cloud cover, precipitation, and winds.

Data and Observations

Table 1

Date	Time	Temp (°C)	Other
	1.		
	2.		
	3.		
	1.		
	2.		
	3.		
	1.		
	2.		
	3.		
	1.		
	2.		
	3.		
	1.		
	2.		
	3.		

Laboratory Activity 2 (continued)

Graph your data showing temperature and time. Graph temperature on the vertical axis and time on the horizontal axis.

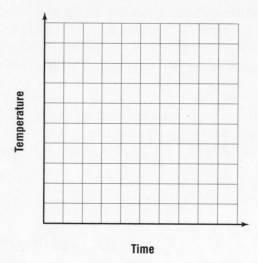

Temperature

Time

Questions and Conclusions

1. Why did you take your air temperature readings in the shade instead of the Sun?

_____

_____

2. Describe any patterns in your air temperature graph.

_____

_____

3. Do these patterns agree with patterns observed by your classmates? Explain.

_____

4. How can you explain the patterns in terms of solar energy absorbed by the land?

_____

_____

Strategy Check

_____ Can you measure air temperature?

_____ Can you collect data for a week?

_____ Can you graph your data?

LAB 1 Laboratory Activity

Effect of Temperature on Cloud Formation

Chapter 16

Clouds are groups of tiny water droplets that are suspended in the air. They form when water condenses around particles in the air. The temperature of the air is one of the factors that affects the type of cloud that forms.

Strategy

You will simulate the formation of a "cloud" inside a soft drink bottle.

You will form a hypothesis that predicts which clouds are denser, those formed by hot air and hot water, or those formed by cold air and cold water.

Materials

large clear plastic bottle with cap (2 L soft drink bottle)
graduated cylinder
thermometer
water (cold)
water (very hot, but not boiling)
matches

Procedure

1. Use the graduated cylinder to measure 60 mL of very cold water. Measure the temperature of the water and record it in the Data and Observations section table. Pour the water into the plastic bottle.

2. Replace and secure the cap. Shake the bottle vigorously for about 10 s. Place the bottle on a firm flat surface.

3. Remove the cap and drop a lighted match into the mouth of the bottle.
   WARNING: *Handle matches carefully.*

4. Replace the cap. Now squeeze the bottle with both hands to increase the internal pressure and observe what happens. Stop squeezing and observe what happens. Squeeze and release the bottle one more time.

5. Record your observations in the Data and Observations section table.

6. Empty the plastic bottle. Measure 60 mL of very hot water. Measure the temperature of the water and record in the Data and Observations section table. Pour the water into the bottle.

7. Hypothesize how your observations will differ using hot water.

8. Repeat steps 3, 4, and 5.

Laboratory Activity 1 (continued)

Data and Observations

Water Temperature	Observations When Pressure Increased	Observations When Pressure Decreased
1. Cold water		
2. Hot water		

Questions and Conclusions

1. What happened when the match was dropped into the bottle?

_____

_____

2. What happened when the bottle with cold water was squeezed?

_____

_____

3. What happened when the bottle with cold water was released?

_____

_____

4. How did the results obtained using cold and hot water compare? How can you explain these results?

_____

_____

_____

5. Why did a "cloud" form when you stopped squeezing the bottle?

_____

_____

_____

6. What was the purpose of dropping a lighted match into the bottle?

_____

_____

_____

Laboratory Activity 1 (continued)

7. How did your hypothesis compare with the results of this activity?

_____

_____

8. Summarize the process of cloud formation.

_____

_____

_____

_____

_____

_____

Strategy Check

_____ Can you simulate the formation of a cloud inside a soft drink bottle?

_____ Can you predict which clouds are denser, those formed by hot air and hot water, or those formed by cold air and cold water?

Laboratory Activity 2

Wind Power

Chapter 16

Wind is an important renewable energy source. Some of the solar radiation that strikes Earth's atmosphere is changed to heat energy. The alternate heating and cooling of the atmosphere as Earth rotates causes air pressure differences. Air moves from regions of high pressure to regions of low pressure, causing wind. Wind energy can be used to drive generators to produce electricity. Any wind that blows at a constant speed above 12.8 km/h can be used to generate electricity. However, the efficiency of the wind as an energy source also depends on the generating system.

Strategy

You will construct the simple device to measure wind speed.
You will measure the wind speed at different times during the day for a week.
You will evaluate wind as a source of energy.

Materials

cardboard (stiff)
scissors
nylon line (30-cm)
table tennis ball

needle long enough to go through ball
glue or paste
colored marker
graph paper

Procedure

1. Cut out the protractor in Figure 2 and glue it to the cardboard.
2. Thread the nylon line through the needle and push the needle through to the center of the table tennis ball. **WARNING:** *Use care when handling sharp objects.*
3. Tie a knot in the nylon line just above the surface of the ball and glue it to the ball. Glue the free end of the nylon line to the spot marked *Center* on the protractor.
4. Color the nylon line with the colored marker.
5. Test the device by setting it on the edge of the desk. If it is level, the line should cover the 0° mark.
6. Select the windiest area of the school grounds. Block the wind and level the device. See Figure 1. Hold the device level and face the wind. Allow the wind to move the table tennis ball. See Figure 1. The angle made by the nylon line will be the wind speed in degrees. Measure the angle and record it in Table 1.
7. Measure and record the wind speed in degrees three times a day for a week. Use the same site each time. Record your measurements in Table 1.

Figure 1

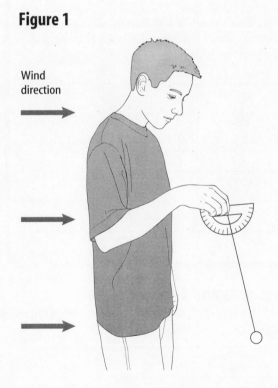

Wind direction

Laboratory Activity 2 (continued)

Data and Observations

Using Table 2, convert your wind speed in degrees to wind speed in kilometers per hour. Fill in the column in Table 1.

Graph the wind speed in kilometers per hour on the vertical axis of the graph paper and graph date/time on the horizontal axis.

Table 1

Date /Time	Wind Speed (degrees)	Wind Speed (km/h)

Table 2

Angle	km /h
0	0
5	9.6
10	13
15	16
20	19.2
25	20.8
30	24
35	25.6
40	28.8
45	32
50	33.6
55	36.8
60	41.6
65	46.4
70	52.8

Questions and Conclusions

1. Is the wind constant in your area? What effect does this have on electricity generation?

_____

_____

_____

2. Estimate how many hours a day you could generate electricity at your site.

_____

Laboratory Activity 2 (continued)

3. What are some advantages to the use of wind power to generate electricity?

_____

4. What are some drawbacks to using wind power?

_____

Strategy Check

_____ Can you construct a device to measure wind speed?

_____ Can you measure wind speed?

_____ Can you evaluate wind as a source of energy?

Figure 2

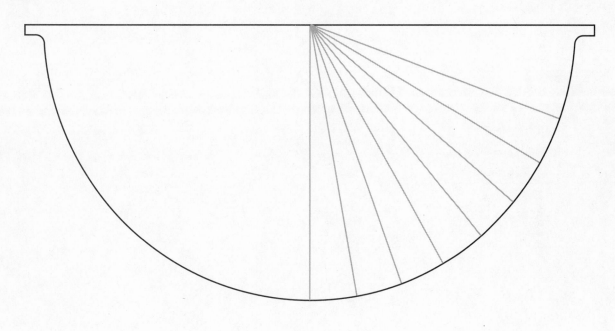

LAB 1 Laboratory Activity

How do the oceans affect climate?

Meteorologists, people who study weather and climate, are always looking at what happens in the oceans. Most of the climate we experience on land is a result of winds and evaporated water at sea. One of the effects of the oceans is to keep the climate near their shores fairly constant. This happens because the water maintains a relatively even temperature. As a result of the weak attractions that form between the hydrogen atoms of one molecule of water and the oxygen atoms of nearby water molecules, a large amount of heat energy can be absorbed by water before its temperature rises. Air molecules do not have this type of attraction between them; therefore the temperature rises more quickly with heat input from the Sun. Volume is also an important consideration in looking at the effects of the Sun's energy on water molecules. It is much easier for the Sun to heat or cool a small pond than it is for the Sun to heat or cool the ocean. In this laboratory exercise, you will compare the effect of the Sun's energy on water with its effect on the atmosphere. From your data, you will make conclusions about climate in different regions.

Strategy

You will model and observe the effect of energy from the Sun on water and on air.
You will infer how oceans and energy from the Sun affect climate.

Materials

2 plastic soda bottles (labels removed)
2 cork or rubber stoppers with center holes
2 long, chemistry-type thermometers
water
paper towels
*100-watt light source (if no sunlight is available)
*apparatus for holding light source stationary
*Alternate materials

Figure 1

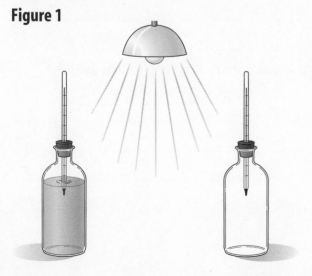

Procedure

1. Work with a partner. Obtain two bottles, stoppers, and thermometers from your instructor. (The thermometers might be fitted into the stopper holes already.)

2. Place the thermometer GENTLY through the stopper hole. The fit should be snug so the stopper will hold the thermometer, but not so tight that it breaks. If your thermometer breaks, DO NOT pick up the pieces of glass yourself. Tell your instructor what happened. If you are uncomfortable doing this step, ask for help from your instructor.

3. Pour water that has reached room temperature into one of your bottles. You do not need to fill the bottle all the way to the top. You need just enough water to insert the thermometer about 8–10 cm into the water. Use paper towels to wipe up any water spills.

4. Check the temperatures on your thermometers and record them on the table provided. They should both be about the same since they are room temperature.

5. If you have a sunny window in your classroom, place your bottles side by side in the window. If possible, it is even better to place your bottles outside in the Sun. If no sunshine is available, place your bottles under a light bulb, as shown in Figure 1.

Laboratory Activity 1 (continued)

6. After 10 min, observe and record the temperatures inside your bottles. If you need to remove the stoppers and thermometers to read the temperature, replace the stoppers quickly or you will lose heat from the bottles.

7. Repeat step 6 two times, so you have a total of four temperature readings for each bottle.

Data and Observations

Table 1

Time of observation in minutes	Temperature of air bottle (°C)	Temperature of water bottle (°C)
Initial time 0		
10		
20		
30		

Questions and Conclusions

1. Which bottle had the greatest amount of temperature change?

_____

_____

2. How do you explain this based on the idea that weak attractions exist between water molecules?

_____

_____

_____

3. How would you relate this temperature change to warm, coastal climates? To flat, inland landscapes, like deserts?

_____

_____

_____

Laboratory Activity 1 (continued)

4. The climate at the North and South Poles is never warm even though they are surrounded by oceans. How do you explain this? [Hint: Think about the angles of the sun's rays.]

_____

_____

_____

_____

_____

Strategy Check

_____ Can you explain how water and air are affected differently by the Sun's energy?

_____ Can you explain how oceans influence climate?

Solar Energy Storage

Chapter 17

Solar energy is not always available when we need it, such as on cloudy days and at night. Storing the solar energy is one of the problems that must be solved before solar energy can be used on a large scale to produce electricity for homes, factories, or businesses. One method of storage involves solids such as rocks. Another method involves the use of water or air.

Strategy

You will construct storage tanks for heat energy.

You will compare the ability of water and gravel to absorb and release heat energy.

You will explain how these storage methods can be used to heat a home.

Materials

2 small coffee cans with lids
water
hot plate
2 nonmercury thermometers
watch with second hand
beaker tongs or pliers
gravel
graph paper
pencils (colored)

Procedure

1. Pour water into one coffee can until it is half full, and set it on the hot plate. **WARNING:** *Use proper protection when handling a hot plate.* Measure the water's temperature near the bottom of the can and near the top. Record the temperatures in Table 1.

2. Turn the hot plate to high and allow it to heat for 2 min. Turn the hot plate off. Measure the temperature of the water near the bottom of the can with one thermometer and close to the top with the other thermometer every minute for 15 min. Record the temperatures in Table 1. **WARNING:** *Do not leave thermometer in can during heating.*

3. Using beaker tongs or pliers, remove the can of water from the hot plate. **WARNING :** *Hot water can cause serious burns.*

4. Allow the hot plate to cool.

5. Pour gravel into the second coffee can until it is half-full, and place it on the hot plate. Measure the temperature near the bottom with one thermometer and near the top of the can with the other thermometer. **WARNING:** *Follow your teacher's instructions on inserting your thermometer into the gravel. Hot gravel can cause serious burns.* Record the temperatures in Table 1.

6. Repeat step 2. This time with gravel instead of water. Allow the can with the gravel to remain on the hot plate until it is completely cool.

Laboratory Activity 2 (continued)

Data and Observations

Table 1

Time (min)	Temperature (°C)			
	Water		Gravel	
	Top	Bottom	Top	Bottom
Prior to heating				

Laboratory Activity 2 (continued)

Directions: *Graph temperature and time for each material. Use a different-colored pencil for each material.*

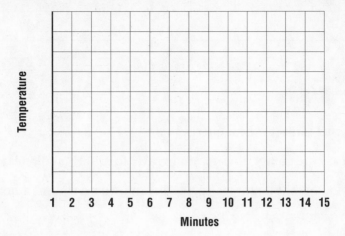

Questions and Conclusions

1. Which material heated more rapidly? How do you know?

_____

_____

2. Which material cooled more rapidly? How do you know?

_____

_____

3. Which material would you choose to store heat energy from a solar collector? Explain.

_____

_____

4. If you use a solar collector that circulates water, you need a large tank of water to store the heat, generally 2.7 L per square meter. How much water would you need to store to heat a house with an area of 1380 m²?

_____

5. How would you store the rocks necessary for a solid solar storage system?

_____

_____

_____

_____

Laboratory Activity 2 (continued)

6. How can you change the storage system to make it more efficient than it is in this activity?

_____

_____

_____

Strategy Check

_____ Can you construct tanks for heat energy?

_____ Can you compare the ability of water and gravel to absorb and release heat energy?

_____ Can you explain how these storage methods can be used to heat a home?

Salt Concentration in Ocean Water

Water in the oceans contains about 3.5 percent salts by weight. Ocean water is salty because water on land dissolves elements such as calcium, magnesium, and sodium on its journey to the oceans. Ions such as sulfate and chloride are brought to the oceans as a result of erupting volcanoes. Sodium and chloride ions, nearly 90 percent of the substances dissolved in ocean water, are what make up table salt. The oceans constantly receive salts and minerals. However, because these substances are used by life forms in the oceans, and they precipitate out, the oceans have not gotten saltier over millions of years.

Strategy

You will consider the effects of a large concentration of salt in soil.
You will determine the presence or absence of dissolved salts and other substances in soil.
You will relate the salt concentration in soil to the salt concentration in ocean water.

Materials

100-mL beaker (3)
salt
coarse sand
clear-plastic storage box
graduated cylinder
distilled water
metric ruler
heat lamp
soil
250-mL beaker (2)
filter paper (or coffee filters)
funnel
watch glass (2)
hot plate
WARNING: *Do not taste, eat, or drink any materials used in the lab.*

Procedure

Part A

1. Mix 100 mL of salt with 100 mL of sand. Pour the mixture into the bottom of the storage box. Add enough water to dissolve the salt. Cover this mixture with a layer of sand 5 cm thick.
2. Set the box under the heat lamp or in a sunny location. **WARNING:** *Do not touch the hot plate or heat lamp.* Allow the box to remain undisturbed overnight.
3. Record your observations, including a sketch, in the Data and Observations section.

Part B

1. Choose two different soil samples from your teacher.
2. Fill a 250-mL beaker up to the 100-mL line with one soil sample. Label this beaker 1.
3. Pour enough distilled water into the beaker to raise the level to the 250-mL mark.
4. Gently stir the sample for 5 min. Take care not to splash any water out.
5. Fold a filter so that it will fit into the funnel.
6. Slowly pour the contents of beaker 1 through the funnel and catch the water in a 100-mL beaker.
7. Pour 30 mL of the water from step 6 into a watch glass and place it on the hot plate.
8. Repeat steps 2 through 7 for soil sample 2.
9. Heat the watch glasses until all the water has evaporated.
10. Record your observations on the next page.

Figure 1

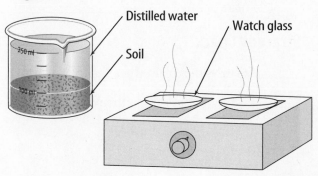

Laboratory Activity 1 (continued)

Data and Observations

Part A

Observations: _____

_____

_____

Sketch

Part B

Observations: _____

_____

_____

Questions and Conclusions

1. If a stream flowed through the sand and salt mixture, what would happen to the salt?

    _____

2. In areas that use river water for irrigation, how could salt become a problem?

    _____

3. What was left on the watch glasses after evaporation was complete?_____

4. Explain how the salt content of the ocean could start to increase over time. _____

    _____

5. On a windy and rainy day, the air tastes salty. What does this tell you about salt in the water

    cycle near oceans? _____

Strategy Check

_____ Can you explain the effect of too much salt in soil?

_____ Can you determine the presence or absence of dissolved salts and other substances in soil?

LAB 2 Laboratory Activity

Floating in Freshwater and in Ocean Water

Chapter 18

Freshwater and ocean water (salt water) have several different physical and chemical properties. One of the properties in which they differ influences how well an object floats. Both freshwater and salt water exert a buoyant force on a floating object.

Strategy

You will compare a boat floating in freshwater with a boat floating in salt water.
You will determine the relationship between the density of a liquid and its buoyant force.
You will observe how salt water and freshwater mix.

Materials

10 cm × 10 cm aluminum foil
25-mL graduated cylinder
clear-plastic storage boxes (2)
ocean water (salt water—make solution with
    salt and water)
freshwater (aged tap water)
grease pencil
metric ruler
50-mL beaker (2)
balance
food coloring
dropper
colored pencils

Procedure

1. Fold the square of aluminum foil into a boat as shown in Figure 1.
2. Half fill one plastic box with salt water. Half fill the other plastic box with freshwater.
3. Float the aluminum boat in the salt water. Mark the waterline on the boat using the grease pencil. Measure the distance from the bottom of the boat to the waterline. Record in Table 1.

4. Float the same aluminum boat in the freshwater. Mark the waterline again.
5. Measure from the bottom of the boat to the new waterline and record.
6. Pour 25 mL of salt water into a beaker. Determine the mass of the salt water. Record the volume and mass in Table 1.
7. Pour 25 mL of freshwater into the second beaker. Determine the mass of the freshwater and record its volume and mass.
8. Color the salt water using food coloring.
9. Using the dropper, add freshwater to the beaker until you see a layer of freshwater on top of the salt water. NOTE: Allow the freshwater to run slowly down the inside wall of the beaker so it does not disturb the salt water. Sketch the layers in the beaker in Table 1.
10. Allow the beaker to stand undisturbed for several days, then observe the results. Sketch the results in Table 1.

Figure 1

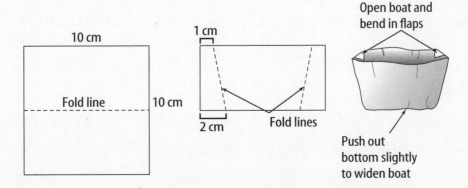

10 cm

Fold line   10 cm

1 cm

2 cm   Fold lines

Open boat and bend in flaps

Push out bottom slightly to widen boat

Laboratory Activity 2 (continued)

Data and Observations

Table 1

	Mass (g)	Volume (cm³)	Depth of Waterline (cm)
Salt Water			
Freshwater			
Beaker (start)		Beaker (after several days)	

Questions and Conclusions

1. In which liquid does the boat float higher? _____

2. State a hypothesis to explain your answer.

   _____

   _____

3. Defend your hypothesis with what you observed about the waterline for each boat.

   _____

4. Why are you able to add a layer of water on top of the salt water?

   _____

5. State the relationship between the density of a liquid and its buoyant force.

   _____

6. Does this confirm or contradict your hypothesis? Explain.

   _____

7. What can happen to two liquids with different densities if they are in contact over a long period of time?

   _____

8. What happens to the water in rivers when the river water flows into the ocean?

   _____

Strategy Check

_____ Can you compare a boat floating in freshwater with a boat floating in salt water?

_____ Can you determine the relationship between the density of a liquid and its buoyant force?

_____ Can you observe how salt water and freshwater mix?

Charting the Ocean Floor

Mapping an ocean or lake floor is much different from mapping a continent. Scientists can't observe and measure underwater the same way they do on land. One way people can find the depth of water is by lowering a weighted rope or chain. When the bottom of the rope or chain hits the ocean or lake floor, the rope or chain will become slack. By measuring how much of the rope or chain is in the water, a person can tell how deep the water is at that spot.

Strategy

You will make a model of the ocean floor, including all the major surface features.

You will make a map of a classmate's model.

Materials

large cardboard box with lid (box should be up to 22 cm wide and 36 cm long; dark paper can be used instead of lid as a cover)

cardboard tubes of various sizes (should be at least 15 cm long)

modeling clay

masking tape

knife or scissors

metric ruler

pen or pencil

string with weight at one end or small chain (should be at least 30 cm longer than depth of box)

Procedure

1. Work with a partner to prepare a model of the ocean floor. First, choose what features you will show. Be sure to include a continental shelf, continental slope, abyssal plain, and mid-ocean ridge. Then use cardboard tubes, modeling clay, and masking tape to form the features of your model along the bottom of the box. Be sure each ocean feature runs from side to side in the box. See Figure 1.

2. After you finish making your model, cut a 1-cm slit in the center of the lid, down its full length. Write your names on the box.

3. Exchange boxes with another pair of classmates. Use your weighted string or chain to "map the ocean floor." At every 1-cm interval along the slit, lower your string or chain.

When it hits the bottom of the "floor," pinch the string or chain gently even with the slit. Keeping your fingers in the same position, pull the string or chain out of the box and measure how deep the string or chain went before touching the bottom. This will give you the depth of the ocean floor at this spot. Record your data in Graph 1.

4. After completing your map, open the box and check your work. How accurate were you in mapping the ocean floor?

Laboratory Activity 1 (continued)

Figure 1

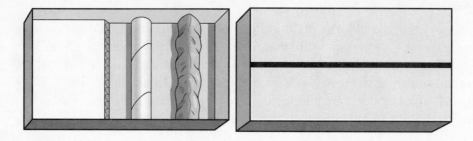

Data and Observations

Graph 1

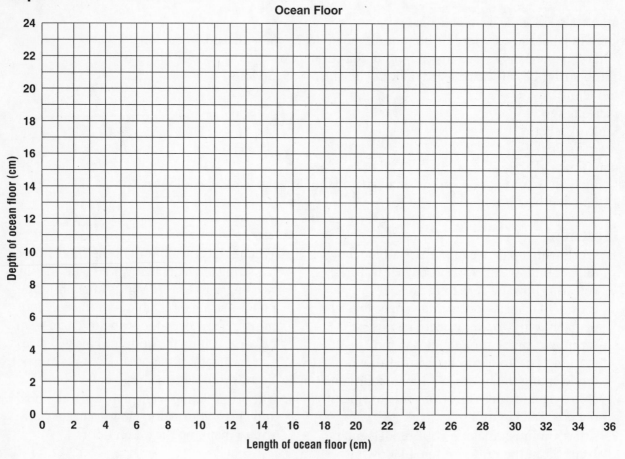

Laboratory Activity 1 (continued)

Questions and Conclusions

1. How accurate was your map?

_____

_____

2. If readings were taken closer together, how would this affect the accuracy of your map?

_____

_____

3. Some error is probably brought about by using a string or chain to measure the ocean depth. How could you improve these readings while still using the same equipment?

_____

_____

_____

4. Give at least two reasons it would be difficult to use these materials to measure distances for a map of the real ocean floor.

_____

_____

_____

_____

Strategy Check

_____ Can you make a realistic model of the ocean floor, including a continental shelf, continental slope, abyssal plain, and mid-ocean ridge?

_____ Can you fairly accurately map a model of the ocean floor?

Photosynthesis and Sunlight

Chapter 19

Green plants on land, in freshwater, and in salt water all share the very special property of being able to manufacture food. All green plants contain chlorophyll, which absorbs light and enables the plant to store energy. If sunlight reaches green plants, they can use two ordinary substances—water and carbon dioxide—to make their own food. Another important product of this reaction is the oxygen that green plants give off when they make food. Plants support all the animals in the world by providing food to eat and oxygen for respiration. This process of taking in water and carbon dioxide, changing light energy into stored energy, and giving off oxygen is called photosynthesis. In ocean waters, photosynthesis usually takes place in the upper 100 meters that sunlight reaches. Scientists interested in knowing how much photosynthesis occurs can measure the amount of oxygen that plants produce under specified conditions and during a defined period of time. They can use this information to calculate how much photosynthesis takes place.

Strategy

You will place one plant under a plant light and a second in the dark, both for 24 hours.

You will measure the amount of oxygen each plant produces.

You will use the amount of oxygen produced to compare the amount of photosynthesis that takes place in plants with and without exposure to light.

Materials

glass jars, each large enough to hold a funnel (2)
water that has stood at room temperature for at least 24 h
balance
sodium bicarbonate (baking soda)
Elodea (aquarium plant)
scissors
metric ruler
glass funnels, small (2)
test tubes, 18 × 150 mm (2)
labels
plant light
*gooseneck lamp with 150-watt bulb
*Alternate materials

Procedure

1. Fill each jar with water that has been standing for at least one day. Add 1 g sodium bicarbonate to the water in each jar.

2. Obtain two *Elodea* plants. Cut about 1 or 2 cm from the bottom of the stem. Throw away the part you cut off.

WARNING: *Always be careful when using scissors.* Using your fingers, lightly crush about 2.5 cm of the cut end of the stem.

3. Place an *Elodea* plant into the water in each jar and cover it with a funnel. Position the plants so that the crushed ends are up. See Figure 1.

Figure 1

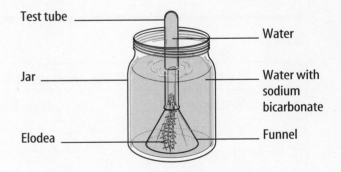

4. Fill a test tube completely with water. Hold your index finger over the mouth of the test tube and invert it over the stem of the funnel. Do not let any water escape from the test tube. NOTE: The test tube must be completely filled with water at the beginning of the experiment. If some water pours out before the test tube is in place, start over again. Place a test tube over each funnel. See **Figure 1.** Label each jar with your name or identifying symbol.

Laboratory Activity 2 (continued)

5. Place one jar near a plant light and leave the light on for 24 hours. Place the other jar in the dark but in a place that has the same conditions, such as temperature, as the jar near the plant light. The plant in the dark is the control.

6. After 24 hours, measure the height in centimeters of the gas column that collected in each test tube. See **Figure 2**. Record this data in **Table 1**.

7. With the other students, copy **Table 2** on the board. Make this table large enough so that every group of students can enter their results in it. Add your results from step 6 to this table.

8. Calculate the average height of the gas column for all of the lab groups. Record this data in **Table 1** in the Data and Observations section.

Figure 2

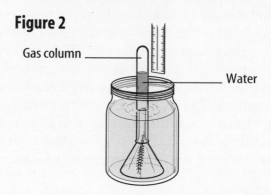

Gas column

Water

Data and Observations

Table 1

Height of Gas Column (mm)				
Light Conditions	My Results	Class Low	Class High	Class Average
Under plant light				
In the dark				

Table 2

Class Data for Height of Gas Column (mm)		
Student's Name	Under Plant Light	In the Dark

Questions and Conclusions

1. Examine the class data in the table written on the board.
   a. What are the highest and lowest amounts of oxygen produced by the plants in the dark?

   _____

   b. What are the highest and lowest amounts of oxygen produced by the plants in the light?

   _____

   c. Compare the average results of the plants in the dark and of the plants in the light.

   _____

Laboratory Activity 2 (continued)

2. What information from this experiment shows that light is needed for photosynthesis?

_____

_____

3. What proof do you have that oxygen is being given off during this experiment? Before you answer, carefully review what you observed during this experiment.

_____

4. Why was sodium bicarbonate added to the water? HINT: Sodium bicarbonate gives off carbon dioxide when mixed with water.

_____

_____

5. Identify the substances in this activity that the *Elodea* plant used for photosynthesis.

_____

6. Identify where the two products of photosynthesis accumulated in this experiment.

_____

The graph in **Figure 3** shows the total amount of oxygen given off by a green plant during a 24-h period. Use the graph to answer questions 7 and 8.

Figure 3

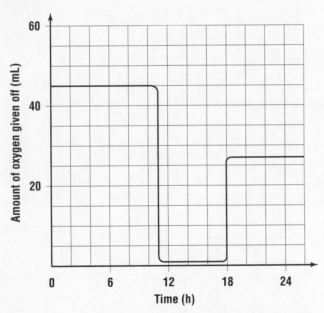

7. **a.** How many hours during the first 24 hours did the plant receive light? Explain.

_____

b. How many hours was the plant in the dark? Explain.

_____

Laboratory Activity 2 (continued)

8. a. Describe the difference in the amount of oxygen the plant produced per hour from hours 1 through 11 and from hours 18 through 24.

_____

_____

b. What difference in light conditions might explain this difference?

_____

_____

c. What might produce a similar difference between the production of two of the same kind of green plants in the ocean?

_____

_____

_____

9. What role do green plants play in the ocean waters?

_____

_____

_____

Strategy Check

_____ Can you measure the amount of oxygen produced by a plant in light and a plant in the dark?

_____ Can you compare the amount of photosynthesis that takes place in each plant?

Human Impact on the Environment

Human beings are changing the environment, and the rate at which they are changing it is increasing rapidly as the population increases. Only recently have people become aware of their impact on the atmosphere, water, and the crust of Earth.

Strategy

You will make a survey of your neighborhood or town to observe people's impact on the environment.

You will use the accompanying matrix to estimate the ways in which humans have affected your local environment.

You will suggest some ways people can change their impact on the environment.

Materials

clipboard
pencil

Procedure

1. Look over the check sheet on the next two pages. A, B, C, and D are general categories for the way people change the environment. Across the top are the various areas of the environment that may be affected by the processes and materials that people use.

2. Walk through your neighborhood (in the city, at least a 10-block square) taking the sheet with you.

3. Place a check after each type of environmental influence found in your neighborhood. For example, if new houses are being built, put a check after "houses," category A.

4. In the boxes to the right, put a diagonal slash under the area(s) affected by this influence. If the effect is good, put a plus in the lower right part of the box. If you think the effect is bad, place a minus in this position.

5. In the upper left of the box, place a number from 1 to 10 to indicate how much impact you think the change has had or will have. If you think the change is small, write in 1; if you think it is or will be very large, write in 10. Use your judgment and observations to assign numbers 2 through 9 on this impact scale.

6. Find your total for each influence and for each affected area. Record your totals in the chart.

7. Find the class total for each influence and for each affected area. Record those totals in the chart.

Laboratory Activity 1 (continued)

Data and Observations

Table 1

	Biological	Scenic	Recreation	Temperature	Air	Water	Eutrophication	Other	Totals
A. Construction									
(Example)		2 / +				3 / -	1 / -		2 / -
Houses									
Roads									
Transmission Lines									
Fences or other barriers									
Canals									
Dams									
Shore structures									
Cut and fill									
Tunnels									
Mines									
Industrial plants									
Landscaped lawns									
B. Traffic									
On roads									
Pipelines									
C. Chemicals									
Fertilization									
Weed and insect control									
Deicing highways									

Laboratory Activity 1 (continued)

Table 2

	Biological	Scenic	Recreation	Temperature	Air	Water	Eutrophi-cation	Other	Totals
D. Waste Disposal									
Litter and dumps									
Sewage									
Stack and exhaust emissions									
Cooling water discharge									
Used lubricant									
Totals									
Class Totals									

Questions and Conclusions

1. List three ways in which the construction of concrete pavement (roads) changes the environment.

_____

_____

2. How does an automobile affect the atmosphere?

_____

3. What other methods of travel, other than automobile would have less adverse effects on the environment?

_____

_____

4. If there is smog in your local area, what is its source?

_____

5. What can be done to reduce or eliminate the smog?

_____

_____

6. What resources are being used in local construction?

_____

Laboratory Activity 1 (continued)

7. What resources are lost to humans when cities move into the surrounding countryside?

_____

_____

8. Are there alternatives?

_____

_____

_____

_____

9. Discuss the drawbacks of the alternatives you have listed in the questions above.

_____

_____

_____

_____

_____

Strategy Check

_____ Can you recognize human influence on your local environment?

_____ Can you estimate the impact, good or bad, using the matrix?

_____ Can you suggest and evaluate alternatives?

LAB 2 Laboratory Activity

Reclamation of Mine Wastes

Chapter 20

Mine wastes, which seem to be worthless, can be made profitable. For example, copper metal can be reclaimed from copper mine waste. When open pit copper is crushed and smelted, copper(II) sulfate is left in the waste rock. The copper(II) sulfate can be dissolved in water. Then more metallic copper can be removed by reacting the copper(II) sulfate with iron ores.

Strategy

You will investigate a process by which copper is reclaimed from open pit waste.
You will determine whether reclaiming copper is profitable.

Materials

copper(II) sulfate crystals, $CuSO_4$
balance
beaker (500-mL)
graduated cylinder (50-mL)
water
litmus paper (blue)
nails (iron scraps)

Procedure

1. Place 3 g of copper(II) sulfate in the beaker. **WARNING:** *Copper(II) sulfate is poisonous. Avoid contact with skin.*

2. Cover the copper(II) sulfate crystals with 50 mL of water. Record the color of the solution in Table 1. Test with litmus paper. Record your results in Table 1.

3. Place the iron scrap in the solution. Observe and record what happens in Table 1.

4. Test the solution with blue litmus paper and record your results in Table 1.

Data and Observations

Table 1

Solution	Color	Litmus	Other Observations
Copper(II) sulfate			
Copper(II) sulfate and iron			

Laboratory Activity 2 (continued)

Questions and Conclusions

1. Why did you add water to the copper(II) sulfate crystals?

_____

_____

2. What happens to the copper in the solution when iron is added?

_____

_____

3. Is this a chemical or physical method of reclaiming the copper?

_____

_____

4. What happened to the water in which the copper(II) sulfate is dissolved?

_____

_____

5. Does this method use up all the waste material?

_____

_____

6. What might happen to a stream if large amounts of the water used in this reclaiming process were flushed into it?

_____

_____

7. What might happen to an abandoned copper mine in a humid climate?

_____

_____

Strategy Check

_____ Can you recognize the copper deposit on the iron?

_____ Could copper be reclaimed from waste using this method?

_____ Would reclaiming the copper be profitable?

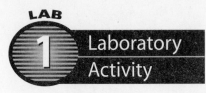

Water Purification

LAB 1 Laboratory Activity

Chapter 21

Pure water is essential to all life forms. But what about a situation in which you do not have pure water available? Life rafts on boats are equipped with an apparatus that can be used to distill water from salt water. Desert safety survival rules provide another means to distill water.

Strategy

You will purify water by using a simple distillation process.
You will discuss how this process could be used in an emergency situation.

Materials

2 coat hangers, or bendable wire
sand (fine) or soil
water
cereal bowl

pen (felt-tip)
pan (larger than the circumference of the bag)
plastic bag (clear)
sunlamp or bright sunshine

Procedure

1. Bend the coat hangers into a frame. See Figure 1.
2. Mix the sand or soil into water in the cereal bowl. Mark the water level on the inside with the pen.
3. Place the cereal bowl in the pan and place the wire frame over it.
4. Pull the plastic bag over the frame until it touches the pan. Record the appearance of the water.

5. Set the apparatus in direct sun or under a sunlamp.
6. Allow the apparatus to stand undisturbed. After about 10 min and again after 30 min, observe and record your observations in Table 1.

Figure 1

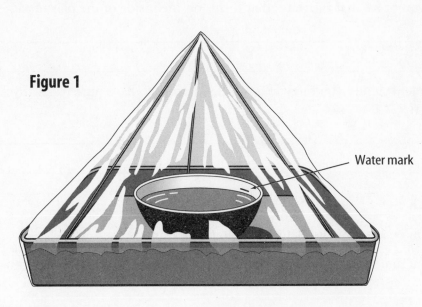

Water mark

Laboratory Activity 1 (continued)

Data and Observations

Table 1

Time (min)	Observations
1. 0	water level _____ inside of plastic bag _____
2. 10	water level _____ inside of plastic bag _____
3. 30	water level _____ inside of plastic bag _____

Questions and Conclusions

1. What happened to the water level in the cereal bowl?

_____

2. Why did water form on the inside of the plastic bag?

_____

_____

3. What two processes are involved in this activity? Identify the energy source.

_____

_____

4. How could you prove that the water that forms on the inside of the plastic bag is pure?

_____

_____

5. What equipment should you carry in a vehicle in order to have pure water if you are going to cross a desert?

_____

_____

Strategy Check

_____ Can you observe the distillation of water by natural processes?

_____ Can you understand how this process could be used in an emergency situation?

Air Pollution

The number of particles floating in the air has increased over the last 20 to 30 years. Many of these particles contribute to the pollution of the air we breathe. The United States has a standard method for reporting the degree of pollution in the air. This is called the Air Quality Index (AQI). The index measures the concentration of pollutants produced by industries, automobiles, and other urban activities. The weather section of a newspaper often states a city's AQI. Along with the AQI number, newspapers often report the major pollutants such as ozone, nitrogen oxide, or particulate matter. It is especially important for elderly people and people who have breathing problems to be aware of this information so they can avoid spending too much time outside in polluted air, which would increase the levels of toxic pollutants in their bodies. It is also important for everyone to know because when people exercise they breathe quickly, and might take in too many pollutants through their lungs. In this activity you will predict and graph air pollution levels in your region over a year's time. Then you will analyze your data.

Air Quality Index

0–50 = Good
51–100 = Moderate
101–150 = Unhealthy for sensitive groups
151–200 = Unhealthy
201–300 = Very unhealthy

Strategy

You will predict the times of year the air quality is best and worst.
You will graph the AQI data for your area during this past year.
You will observe trends and analyze the data.

Materials

list of data from teacher
graph paper

Procedure

1. Predict the quality of the air in the area where you live. At what times of the year do you think it is the best? The poorest?

2. Your teacher has a list of air quality data for the last year for your city or a city in your area. Obtain the data from your teacher.

3. Review the data. Then use graph paper to graph the data. On your graph, mark the air quality number for the 1st and 15th of each month as provided. Place the dates on the horizontal axis and the index numbers on the vertical axis.

4. When you have finished marking all the data points on your graph, connect them with a line. The line will help you see the changes in air quality from month to month.

Laboratory Activity 2 (continued)

Data and Observations

1. What is the highest number on your air quality index graph? In what month does it occur?

_____

2. What is the lowest number on your air quality index graph? In what month does it occur?

_____

3. Do you see a trend? Explain.

_____

Questions and Conclusions

1. During what season was the air quality the best? How do you know?

_____

2. During what season was the air quality the poorest? How do you know?

_____

3. How can you explain your results in terms of the Sun's energy?

_____

4. Many people take vacations during the summer months. Might this affect air quality? Explain your answer.

_____

_____

5. In what parts of the country would you expect the air quality to be the best? The poorest? Explain your answer.

_____

_____

6. In the Air Quality Index, what people do you think make up the sensitive groups?

_____

7. Overall, how would you rate the air quality of your region or city? Explain your answer.

_____

_____

Strategy Check

_____ Can you predict what times of year the air quality is poorest?

_____ Can you graph the year's AQI data for your area?

_____ Can you observe how air quality changes from month to month?

Star Colors

Laboratory Activity 1

In 1665, Isaac Newton demonstrated that sunlight is composed of many colors. Today the spectra of a star is one of the most important tools scientists use to determine the star's surface temperature and composition. The Draper system of spectral classification is used in this activity.

Strategy

You will define the term *star*.
You will observe and record star colors.
You will classify stars based on their color.

Materials

binoculars or telescope (optional)
graph paper

Procedure

1. On a clear, bright night observe the stars with your eyes or with the binoculars or telescope.
2. Use some landmarks and divide the sky into four sections. Label the landmarks in the diagram under Data and Observations.
3. Observe and record the color of each star in each section. Record your observations on your diagram under Data and Observations.
4. Using the information in Table 1, compile your data in a table showing the star color, spectral type, and number of stars in each section. Set up your table on one end of your graph paper.
5. Under the table on the graph paper, draw a bar graph showing the star spectral types and the number of stars in each spectral type.

Table 1

Draper's Star Classification Chart		
Star spectral type	Color	Surface temperature (K)
M	red	2,000–4,000
K	red to orange	3,500–5,000
G	yellow	5,000–6,000
F	yellow-white	6,000–7,500
A	white	9,000
B	bluish-white	11,000–25,000
O	bluish-white	60,000

Laboratory Activity 1 (continued)

Data and Observations

Diagram night sky here.

Questions and Conclusions

1. What property did you use to classify a celestial body as a star?

_____

2. Which star spectral type is the most abundant?

_____

3. Which star spectral type is our Sun?

_____

4. What is the surface temperature of our Sun?

_____

5. The temperature of stars is given in Kelvins. Changing from the Celsius scale to the Kelvin scale is very easy: $K = °C + 273°$. What is the temperature of the Sun in Celsius degrees?

_____

Strategy Check

_____ Can you define the term *star*?

_____ Can you observe and record the colors of the stars?

_____ Can you classify stars based on their color?

Star Positions

When you watch the stars on a clear night, do you get the impression that you are in an upside-down bowl? The ancient Greeks believed that the stars were fixed to a clear bowl that slowly rotated around Earth. Although today we know that Earth rotates, the celestial sphere is still a good model to use to locate stars and other celestial bodies.

Strategy

You will construct a model of the north celestial hemisphere.
You will plot the stars on the celestial sphere.

Materials

globe (mounted)
hemisphere (clear plastic or terrarium top)

pen (felt-tip)
string to go around celestial equator

Procedure

1. The celestial sphere appears to move around a line that is an extension of Earth's axis. The north and south celestial poles are the points where Earth's geographic axis intersects the celestial sphere. See Figure 1. Label the north celestial pole with a dot on the inside of the hemisphere.

2. The celestial equator is the intersection of a plane that passes through Earth's equator and the celestial sphere. Place the clear hemisphere over the globe so that the north pole and the north celestial pole are in line. Mark the celestial equator on the hemisphere. The celestial equator is 90° from the celestial poles. See Figure 1.

3. Planes comparable to latitude on Earth are called *declination* on the celestial sphere. Positions north of the celestial equator are called *plus declination* and are measured in degrees. Positions south of the celestial equator are called *minus declination,* also measured in degrees.

4. The celestial circles that correspond to longitude on Earth are called *right ascension.* Right ascension is measured from the point where the sun crosses the celestial equator about March 21 (the vernal equinox).

5. Right ascension is measured in hours, minutes, and seconds, moving eastward from the vernal equinox. On the equator, 15 degrees of arc equals 1 hour.

Figure 1

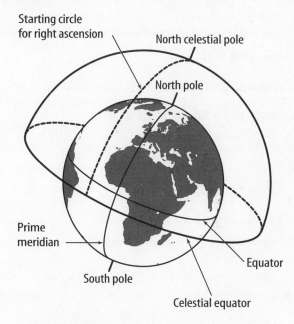

Take a length of string and measure the distance around the celestial equator in centimeters. Record your answer in the Data and Observations section. Divide this distance by 24. Measure and mark these spaces around the celestial equator. Each mark represents 1 hour. Start at the prime meridian and move eastward around the celestial equator. See Figure 1.

6. Now you have a grid system similar to latitude and longitude.

7. Map the locations of the stars in Table 1 on the celestial sphere.

Laboratory Activity 2 (continued)

Table 1

Common name	Scientific name	R. A. hr	min	Dec. (°)
Vega	Lyrae	18	36	38
Arcturus	Bootes	14	15	19
Altair	Aquilae	19	50	8
Betelgeuse	Orionis	05	55	7
Aldebaran	Tauri	04	35	16
Deneb	Cygni	20	41	45
Regulus	Leonis	10	08	12
Castor	Geminorum	07	34	32

Data and Observations

Celestial equator = _____ cm

Questions and Conclusions

1. How is right ascension like longitude?

   _____

   How is it different?

   _____

2. Compare declination to latitude.

   _____

3. What does the vernal equinox on the celestial sphere correspond to on geographic maps?

   _____

4. Why are different stars visible during the year?

   _____

5. Why can't you see a star with a minus declination from the northern hemisphere?

   _____

Strategy Check

_____ Can you construct a model of the north celestial hemisphere?

_____ Can you locate stars on the celestial sphere?

Earth's Spin

The speed at which Earth turns on its axis can be described in two ways. The velocity of rotation refers to the rate at which Earth turns on its axis. Velocity of rotation refers to Earth as a whole. For any point on Earth's surface, the speed of Earth's rotation can be described as its instantaneous linear velocity. This velocity is the speed of the point as it follows a circular path around Earth.

Strategy

You will determine the instantaneous linear velocity of some points on Earth.
You will compare the linear velocities of points at different locations on Earth.

Materials

globe (mounted on axis)   meterstick
tape (adhesive)   stopwatch
string

Procedure

Part A

1. Place small pieces of adhesive tape on the globe along the Prime Meridian at the equator, at 30° N latitude, at 60° N latitude, and at the North Pole.
2. Line up the tape with the metal circle above the globe; see Figure 1.
3. With your finger on the globe, move it west to east for one second; see Figure 2.
4. For each location marked by tape, measure the distance from the Prime Meridian to the metal circle. Use the string and the meterstick to get accurate distances.

Record the distances in Table 1.
5. Realign the metal circle with the pieces of tape. Move the globe west to east for 2 s. Record the distances from the tapes to the metal circle in Table 1.
6. Repeat step 5, moving the globe for 3 s. Record your results in Table 1.

Part B

Calculate the speed of each point for each trial. Record the speeds in Table 2. Use the formula:
velocity (cm/s) = distance (cm)/time (s)

Figure 1

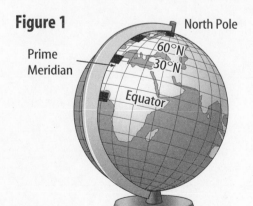

Figure 2

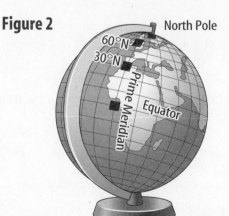

Laboratory Activity 1 (continued)

Data and Observations

Table 1

Latitude	Distance (cm)		
	1 s	2 s	3 s
Equator			
30° N			
60° N			
North Pole			

Table 2

Latitude	Velocity (cm/s)		
	Trial 1	Trial 2	Trial 3
Equator			
30° N			
60° N			
North Pole			

Questions and Conclusions

1. Which point moved the farthest distance in all three trials?

_____

2. Which point moved the least distance in all three trials?

_____

3. Which point did not move at all in the three trials?

_____

4. On what does the linear velocity of a point depend?

_____

5. How does the linear velocity change as you move from the equator to the poles?

_____

Strategy Check

_____ Can you determine instantaneous linear velocity?

_____ Can you see that the linear velocity is not the same for all points on Earth?

Earth's Shape

You've probably seen photographs of Earth taken by satellites in space. Such photographs clearly show Earth's round shape. Early astronomers didn't have spacecraft to help them study Earth. They had to rely on observation and measurement. In this activity, you'll explore some methods used by early astronomers to determine Earth's true shape.

Strategy

You will demonstrate evidence of Earth's shape.
You will describe the type of shadow cast by Earth during a lunar eclipse.

Materials

small piece of cardboard
scissors
basketball
flashlight
textbook

Procedure

1. Cut out a triangular piece of cardboard so that each side measures approximately 6 cm.
2. Hold a basketball at eye level about 33 cm from your eye. Have your partner slowly move the cardboard up and over the basketball from the opposite side.
3. In the space below, sketch the cardboard as it appears when the top of the cardboard first comes in sight over the basketball.

Make another sketch of the cardboard as it appears when fully visible above the basketball.

4. Darken the room. Use a flashlight to cast a shadow of a textbook against the wall. Do the same for the basketball. In the space below, draw the shadows of the textbook and the basketball.

Data and Observations

Laboratory Activity 2 (continued)

Questions and Conclusions

1. Compare and contrast your two drawings of the cardboard.

_____

_____

_____

2. How were your different views of the cardboard similar to the view of a ship on the horizon approaching shore?

_____

_____

3. How did the cardboard activity demonstrate evidence of Earth's shape?

_____

_____

_____

4. Compare and contrast your drawings of the shadows cast by the basketball and the textbook.

_____

_____

5. During a lunar eclipse, Earth casts a shadow on the Moon. What type of shadow would Earth cast if it were flat? What type of shadow does Earth cast on the Moon during a lunar eclipse?

_____

_____

6. How do the shadows you observed demonstrate evidence of Earth's shape?

_____

_____

_____

7. Can you think of any other evidence that demonstrates Earth's round shape? Describe this evidence.

_____

_____

Strategy Check

_____ Can you demonstrate evidence of Earth's shape?

_____ Can you describe the type of shadow cast by Earth during a lunar eclipse?

Venus—The Greenhouse Effect

LAB 1 Laboratory Activity

Because Venus is closer to the Sun, it receives almost twice the amount of solar radiation received by Earth. However, because of its clouds Venus reflects more radiation in to space than does Earth. We might expect Venus, therefore, to have surface temperatures similar to Earth's. However, the Pioneer vehicles to Venus have measured surface temperatures of 460°C. Some scientists explain this high temperature as the "greenhouse effect." When the solar energy strikes the surface of Venus, the energy is absorbed and changed into heat energy. This heat energy is reflected back to the atmosphere where it is trapped.

Strategy

You will build a model to show the greenhouse effect.

You will compare this model to Earth.

You will form a hypothesis about temperatures on Venus using data collected from this model and from the *Pioneer* spacecraft.

Materials

soil
clear plastic storage box and lid
cardboard (stiff)

thermometer
heat lamp (mounted)
watch

graph paper
pencils (colored)

Figure 1

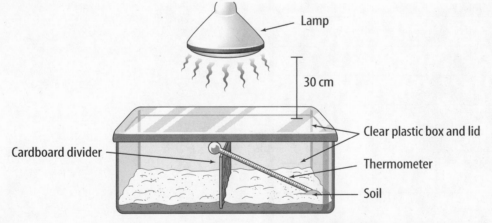

Lamp

30 cm

Clear plastic box and lid

Cardboard divider

Thermometer

Soil

Procedure

1. Place about 3 cm of soil in the bottom of the clear plastic box.
2. Thoroughly moisten the soil with water.
3. Cut the piece of cardboard so that it makes a divider for the box. The cardboard should not quite reach the top of the box. Insert the divider into the box.
4. Lean the thermometer against the divider with the bulb end up. (See Figure 1) Put the lid on the box.
5. Position the box and lamp in an area of the room where no direct sunlight reaches. **WARNING:** *Use care handling heat lamp.*

6. Place the heat lamp about 30 cm above the box and direct the light so it shines on the thermometer bulb.
7. Turn off the lamp and allow the thermometer to return to room temperature. Record room temperature under Data and Observations.
8. Turn on the lamp and measure the temperature every minute for 20 min. Record the temperatures in Table 1.
9. Turn off the lamp and allow the thermometer to return to room temperature. Remoisten the soil and repeat step 8 without the lid. Record your data in Table 1.

Laboratory Activity 1 (continued)

Data and Observations

Room temperature: _____

Table 1

Time (min)	Temperature (°C)	
	Lid On	Lid Off
1		
2		
3		
4		
5		
6		
7		
8		
9		
10		
11		
12		
13		
14		
15		
16		
17		
18		
19		
20		

On a separate piece of paper, graph the data using two different colors. Plot Temperature on the vertical axis and Time on the horizontal axis.

Laboratory Activity 1 (continued)

Questions and Conclusions

1. Did the temperature increase the most with the lid on or off? Why?

_____

_____

_____

2. Draw a diagram of Earth showing its atmosphere and what occurs due to solar radiation in the atmosphere. List the components of Earth's atmosphere on your diagram. Write a brief explanation of the greenhouse effect on Earth.

_____

_____

_____

3. Compare the greenhouse effect of the activity to the greenhouse effect on Earth. How are they similar? How are they different?

_____

_____

_____

_____

_____

Laboratory Activity 1 (continued)

4. Venus's atmosphere is composed mainly of carbon dioxide, carbon monoxide, water, nitrogen, and sulfuric acid. Venus's atmosphere is 100 times more dense than Earth's atmosphere. From the surface of Venus up to 20 km, there appears to be a clear region of atmosphere. A thick layer of clouds extends from about 50 km to 80 km above the surface of Venus. These clouds are composed of drops of sulfuric acid. Above and below these clouds are other, thinner layers of haze. Venus's ionosphere extends from 100 km to 200 km above the surface. Like the ionosphere of Earth, it has layers. The temperature in the ionosphere of Venus is cooler than the temperature in Earth's ionosphere.

   Draw a diagram of Venus showing its atmosphere and what happens to solar radiation in the atmosphere. List the components of Venus's atmosphere on your diagram. Write a brief explanation of the greenhouse effect on Venus.

   _____

   _____

   _____

   _____

5. Compare the greenhouse effect on Earth and Venus. Can you think of a reason why the surface of Venus is so much hotter than the surface of Earth?

   _____

   _____

   _____

   _____

Strategy Check

_____ Can you build a model to show the greenhouse effect?

_____ Can you compare this model to Earth?

The Behavior of Comets

Chapter 24

One way scientists study the behavior and composition of comets is by observing them as they orbit the Sun. Observations made through telescopes and pictures sent back by space probes have led scientists to believe a comet is a mixture of ice and rock. Heat from the Sun vaporizes some of the comet's ice, which releases bits of rock and dust that form a cloud around the comet. Solar winds blowing on the cloud create the comet's tail. The intensity of the solar wind makes the tail point away from the Sun, no matter which direction the comet is facing. Because the comet is vaporizing when it becomes visible from Earth, each time we see a comet, we are witnessing its deterioration.

Strategy

You will model and observe the behavior of comets orbiting the Sun.

You will describe the behavior and draw inferences about the life of a comet based on your observations.

Materials

newspaper
small electric fan
books or boxes
waxed paper
ruler

red, green, or blue construction paper
   (the color should make water drops easy to see)
sand (not dirt)
ice (crushed, not in cubes)

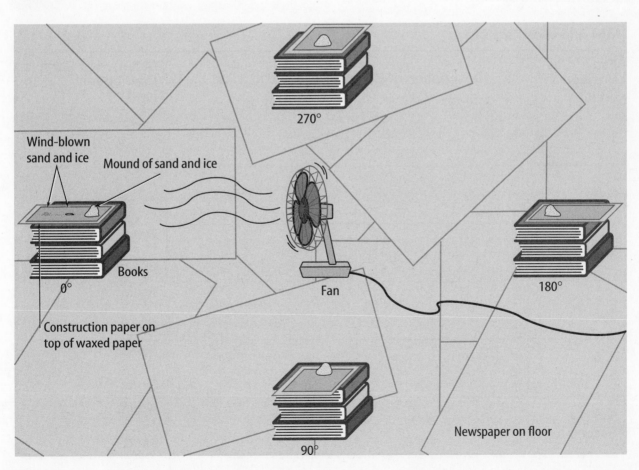

Laboratory Activity 2 (continued)

Procedure

1. Working in groups of four students, place newspaper on your lab table or the floor near an electric outlet. Put the fan in the middle of the newspaper. Place books or boxes at four positions around the fan. The first position should be 0° The next are at 90°, 180°, and 270°. Be sure to cover books with wax paper to protect them against any water spills.

2. Take a piece of colored construction paper about 23 cm × 15 cm and place it with its longer edge away from the fan. Do this for each position. See Figure 1. Then get a small mixture (about a tablespoon) of sand and ice and mound it on the paper at the end nearest the fan. Draw a line on the page around the mound of sand and ice.

3. Have one student carefully turn on the fan at the 0° position and observe the effect the blowing wind has on the ice/sand mixture.

Let the fan run for three minutes and then turn it off. Record your observation in the table provided.

4. Turn the fan so that it is pointing to the 90° position and repeat the procedure. Continue until the fan has run on all four positions and then repeat for position 0°. Turn the fan to the 90° position. Carefully turn on the fan one more time. Be sure to record all your observations in the table.

5. When you are finished, take your paper and carefully place it on the ground or tabletop. Try not to move any of the particles as you move the paper. Take your ruler and measure the distance the water drops and sand moved from their original position at the front of the paper. Record these distances in the last column of the table.

Data and Observations

Fan Position (deg.)	Description of Behavior of Ice and Sand	Distance of Particle Distribution (cm)
1. 0°		
2. 90°		
3. 180°		Water: Sand:
4. 270°		Water: Sand:
5. 0° Second trial		Water: Sand:
6. 90° Second trial		Water: Sand:

Laboratory Activity 2 (continued)

Questions and Conclusions

1. What is one behavior of the ice and sand you observed?

_____

_____

_____

2. How would you explain what you saw?

_____

_____

_____

3. How does this behavior demonstrate the similarities between your experiment and what we observe in a comet orbiting the Sun?

_____

_____

_____

4. Where does the water and dust from a melting comet go?

_____

_____

5. Using your answer from question 4, would you expect a comet to always die out? Explain your answer.

_____

_____

_____

Strategy Check

_____ Can you model the behavior of a comet orbiting the Sun?

_____ Can you describe this behavior based on what you know about the composition of comets?

Absolute and Apparent Magnitudes

Chapter 25

The apparent magnitude of a star, or how much light is received on Earth, can be confusing to an astronomer trying to measure the distance a star is from Earth. Apparent magnitude is much different from the absolute magnitude, which is the true measure of how much light the star emits. These two variables control the brightness of the stars we see in our night sky. The absolute magnitude is not the same for every star. It is determined by the amount of light it gives off. The second variable is the amount of light received on Earth. The mixing of these two variables can lead to misunderstanding about the size and distance of a star. That is why it is important to understand the characteristics of stars and light to be able to correctly determine what we see in the night sky.

Strategy

You will observe how light behaves over distance.
You will predict how two stars that are different in size and far away from each other may appear in the night sky.

Materials

black construction paper
scissors
small flashlight

rubber bands
medium sized nail
tape

measuring tape or meterstick
white correction fluid
*chalk
* markers
* Alternate materials

Procedure

1. Students will work in groups of three to four. Use your scissors to cut a piece of black construction paper large enough to comfortably cover the light end of the flashlight.

2. Cover the end of the flashlight with the paper and secure it in place with a rubber band. Take the sharp end of the nail and carefully poke a single hole in the center of the paper covering. The smaller the hole the better.

3. Find a wall or hard surface on which you can tape a background of more black construction paper. An area about one meter square would be best for the experiment. An alternate choice would be to use the black- or white-board in the classroom. If you do use a wall, write only with the appropriate materials, such as chalk or erasable marker.

4. At a distance of two meters or six feet from the wall, mark a spot with tape on the ground. Then mark the next interval at 1.3 meters or four feet. The last mark is at 0.6 meters or two feet.

Figure 1

5. Ask your instructor to darken the room as much as possible. One student will stand at the six foot mark and turn on the flashlight. The other students will mark the edges of the diameter of the circle of light made by the flashlight with correction fluid, chalk, or markers. Be sure to notice the intensity of the inner and outer regions of the circle of light. You will record this in the data table provided.

Laboratory Activity 1 (continued)

6. Repeat this procedure at the closer interval. Then repeat one more time at the closest interval. Look at the intensity of the light instead. When is it most intense and where is it very diffuse? Record these observations in your table.

7. Observe the behavior of light at different intervals. Try to account for what you observe by what you know. For instance, you know the amount of light exiting the flashlight has not changed at all during the experiment. So what is happening to the dispersal of light? Record your hypothesis in the space marked "Hypothesis for the dispersal of light."

Data and Observations

Table 1

Diameter of Light Circle (cm)			Observations about Intensity of Light (cm)
Trial 1	Trial 2	Trial 3	

Laboratory Activity 1 (continued)

According to your experiment, your circle of light changed in size as you got closer to the wall. The intensity, or brightness, also changed. How would you account for this? Write your hypothesis in the space below.

Hypothesis for the dispersal of light: _____

_____

_____

_____

Questions and Conclusions

1. The circle of light produced by your flashlight on the wall was larger when you were farther away from the wall. Was the light more or less intense? How do you account for this?

_____

_____

_____

_____

2. The circle of light got smaller as you approached the wall. Was the light more or less intense? How do you account for this?

_____

_____

_____

_____

3. As a result of your experiment, would you expect a star to appear brighter when closer to or farther from the Earth? Explain your answer.

_____

_____

_____

_____

4. If you used a bigger and brighter flashlight and repeated the same experiment, what would you expect your results to be like? Explain your answer.

_____

_____

_____

_____

Laboratory Activity 1 (continued)

5. Suppose you were going to perform the experiment with two students: One holds a weak flash-light; the other a strong flashlight. How would you place the students so that the circles of light on the wall were exactly the same size? Explain your answer in terms of magnitude.

_____

_____

_____

_____

6. How would you model the difference in absolute magnitude between the two flashlights?

_____

_____

_____

_____

7. Predict what an astronomer would look for if he or she wanted to determine the size and heat of a star and its distance from the Earth. Would it be a good idea to watch the star over a long period?

_____

_____

_____

_____

Strategy Check

_____ Can you observe how light behaves over distance?

_____ Can you predict how two stars that are different in size and far away from each other may appear in the night sky?

LAB 2 Laboratory Activity

Spectral Analysis

The photograph of the spectrum of a star, sorted by color across a plate, will reveal spectral lines upon close examination. The lines are produced by elements in a star at high temperature. These lines represent the chemical composition of the star. Each element has its own "fingerprint." To analyze the spectra of stars, scientists collected spectra of all the known elements. If we compare the spectral lines of an unknown star with the spectral lines of elements, we can determine the chemical composition of the star. More recently, we have discovered not only the composition of the stars but also their temperatures, their rotational rate, and their relative motion with regard to Earth.

Strategy

You will construct a simple spectral analyzer.
You will determine the composition of a star using the spectral analyzer.
You will determine other characteristics of a star by comparing the spectral lines with a standard.

Materials

scissors

Procedure

1. Turn to the third page of this lab. Cut out the pull tab card; the spectroscope finger-prints card; and Stars B, C, and D along the dashed lines.
2. Make five slits along the dashed lines A, B, C, D, and E on the fingerprints card.
3. From left to right, insert "Pull Tab Out" up through slit E, down through slit D, up through slit C, down through slit B, and up through slit A.

4. Compare the lines of each known element with the lines of Star A. If lines match, then that element is present in Star A. Record your findings in Table 1.
5. Star B, Star C, and Star D are provided for further study and comparison. Each can be placed over Star A.

Data and Observations

Table 1

Star	Chemical Composition	Other Characteristics
A		
B		
C		
D		

Laboratory Activity 2 (continued)

Questions and Conclusions

1. When you hear someone say that neon lights look beautiful, what color comes to mind? What color is suggested by the "fingerprints" of neon?

_____

_____

_____

_____

2. Did any of the stars have the same chemical composition? Look at the table.

_____

_____

_____

3. Sometimes scientists see spectral lines that do not fit the usual pattern. The lines might be shifted from their usual positions. This may suggest that the star is moving either toward the observer (shift toward the blue) or away from the observer (shift toward the red). Look at the spectral lines for Star B and Star D. Star B is the standard for comparison. How is Star D different? What is a possible explanation for the difference?

_____

_____

_____

_____

4. If the scientist sees the spectral lines wider than usual, he or she relates this spectral broadening to either rotational speed (the broader the faster), temperature (the broader the hotter), or pressure (the broader the greater pressure). Look at the spectral lines for Star B and Star C. Star B is the standard. How is Star C different? What could be a possible explanation?

_____

_____

_____

_____

Strategy Check

_____ Can you construct a simple spectral analyzer?

_____ Can you determine the composition of a star using the spectral analyzer?

_____ Can you determine other characteristics of a star by comparing the spectral lines with a standard?

Laboratory Activity 2 (continued)

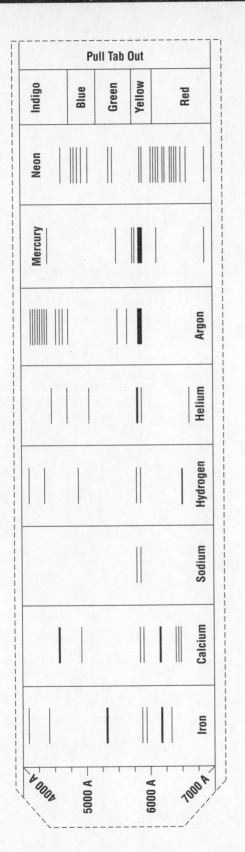

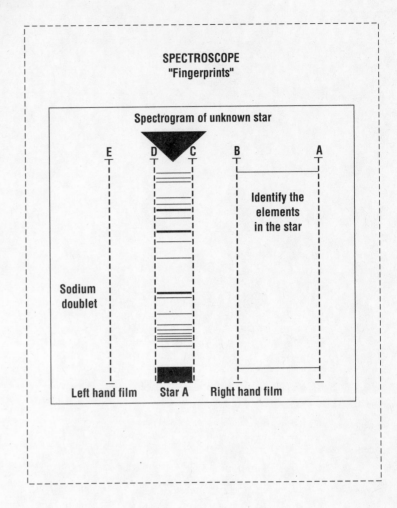

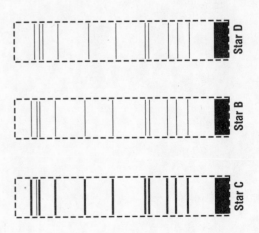

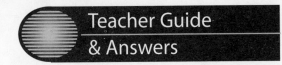
Chapter 1   The Nature of Science

Laboratory Activity 1 (page 1)

Lab Note: Students may need guidance with some of the necessary procedures; cleaning beakers between trials, not filling beakers to the top with water, and using different ice cubes for each trial. Students may also need help with finding the volume of an object using displacement.

Procedure

Data Table

   A. It begins to melt. This results in a mass and volume change.
   B. It is irregular and not a cube.
   C. length × width × height
   D. floats—partially submerged
   E. sinks—more dense than alcohol

2. A. Density: mass per unit volume
     Mass: measure of the amount of matter in an object
     Volume: space that an object fills or occupies

3. First Trial Procedure

   A. find volume by l × w × h
   B. find mass by using balance
   C. divide volume into mass
   D. compare density value to accepted value
   E. find the percent error

Second Trial Procedure

   A. find volume by displacement—in alcohol
   B. same
   C. same
   D. same
   E. same

4. A. Answers will vary.
   B. .9 g/cm³
   C. Answers will vary.
   D. Answers will vary.

5. Answers will vary with student results.

Laboratory Activity 2 (page 3)

Questions and Conclusions

1. probably not; probably not
2. The three trials do not provide enough data for an accurate prediction.
3. yes; A more accurate average is obtained as the amount of data increases.
4. Distances should correlate.
5. class average; The probability of obtaining a useful value increases with more data.
6. no

Chapter 2   Matter

Laboratory Activity 1 (page 7)

Lab Note: Colors in minerals depend largely on impurities. Organic matter gives a black color; iron, red or yellow; manganese, purple. A good reference book for minerals might be useful.

Data and Observations

Sketch A

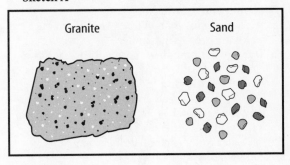

Sketch B

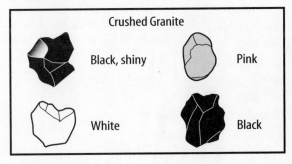

Sketch C

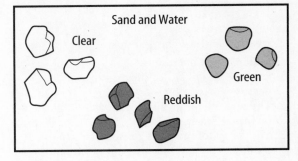

Sketch D

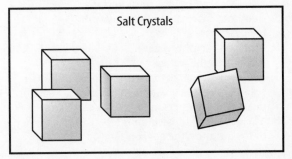

Sketch E

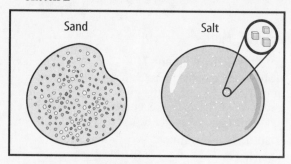

Sand   Salt

Questions and Conclusions

1. yes; Most sands contain fragments of quartz, which are present in granite.
2. They are both mixtures; both salt and sand contain crystals. Saltwater is homogeneous—salt dissolves in water; sand and water is heterogeneous—sand does not dissolve in water.
3. mixture; Salt can be removed by evaporating the water. Salt and water are both compounds, but salt water is not composed of elements in a definite ratio.
4. mixture; Granite is composed of particles that can be recognized. The granite can be separated into simpler substances by mechanical means.
5. evaporation or cooling of solutions; magnetism; sorting by sizes using sieves, filtering of solutions; settling of solutions

Lab Note: You may want to introduce students to distillation as a method of separating mixtures.

Laboratory Activity 2 (page 9)

Data and Observations
Students' answers will vary, but densities should be close to the values given here. Variations can be due to temperature differences.
1. 1.034 g/cm^3 at 4°C
2. 1.0 g/cm^3 at 4°C
3. greater than 1.0 g/cm^3; less than 1.034 g/cm^3

Questions and Conclusions
1. Students' tables for densities;
   density = mass/volume d= m/v
2. The egg sank through the freshwater but floated on the salt water.
3. The density of the egg is greater than that of the freshwater but less than that of the salt water.
4. The egg probably sank as the density of the salt water was reduced by the addition of freshwater.
5. Buoyancy increases as the density of the liquid increases.
6. A person floats in water because the person is less dense than the water.
7. Because seawater is more dense than freshwater, seawater exerts a greater buoyant force. Therefore, it is easier for a person to float in seawater.
8. The density of the helium is less than the density of the air; thus, the balloon floats.

Chapter 3   Minerals

Laboratory Activity 1 (page 11)

Data and Observations
Table 1
Color patterns will vary with the thickness of the crystal and the direction in which the light is traveling through the crystal.

Questions and Conclusions
1. Students should have observed a double image of the letters.
2. Unpolarized light enters the calcite as a single ray and leaves the crystal as two rays.
3. Halite is isometric with only one index of refraction for parallel and perpendicular light.
4. Polarizing resulted in only one image. It separated light in parallel and perpendicular planes. Only one planar surface passed through the crystal.

Lab Note: You might wish to have students examine various thicknesses of mica and compare the color patterns. Students could also examine crystals of sugar, epsom salts, salol (phenyl salicylate), and/or clear pieces of crushed ice.

Laboratory Activity 2 (page 13)

Questions and Conclusions
1. Sand and iron in the syrup; sand is less dense than syrup and stays on top. Iron is heavier than syrup and sinks.
2. A magnet gives a cleaner separation.
3. a mixture
4. A mixture is more like a rock. Minerals are not mixtures.
5. Only the pepper remains on the filter paper; pepper is not soluble, but salt dissolves in the water and passes through the filter paper.
6. The separation of pepper from salt water is by the filtration method.
7. separation by density
8. evaporation of water leaving salt

Chapter 4   Rocks

Laboratory Activity 1 (page 15)

Questions and Conclusions
1. layers of rock precipitated at different times
2. The various layers precipitated at different times.
3. They know that some concretions form around fossils.

Laboratory Activity 2 (page 17)

Lab Note: Rock samples should be numbered as follows: 1. hornfels; 2. gneiss; 3. schist; 4. quartzite; 5. soapstone; 6. phyllite; 7. slate; 8. marble.

Data and Observations
1. hornfels; nonfoliated
2. gneiss; foliated
3. schist; foliated
4. quartzite; nonfoliated

5. soapstone; nonfoliated
6. phyllite; foliated
7. slate; foliated
8. marble; nonfoliated

Lab Note: Drawings should accurately show sample rocks. Descriptions should match drawings and should closely match descriptions in the table in the Procedure section.

Questions and Conclusions

1. Answers will vary, but students may have a hard time distinguishing schist and gneiss.
2. Possible answers: the quantities of various minerals they contain may vary; the degree of change may vary because of being subjected to differing amounts of heat and/or pressure.

Chapter 5   Earth's Energy and Mineral Resources

Laboratory Activity 1 (page 19)

Lab Note: If available, you also may want to include samples of peat or lignite for testing. Coal samples and charcoal briquettes should be about the same size.

Questions and Conclusions

1. Answers will depend on the grade of coal used, but most coal samples should burn longer than most charcoal samples.
2. While actual percentages calculated will vary, the charcoal sample will result in a greater percentage of residue.
3. Coal is the more efficient fuel because it burned longer and produced less residue.
4. Anthracite coal would be a more efficient fuel because it has a more concentrated carbon content. It should burn longer and produce less residue than either of the samples tested.

Laboratory Activity 2 (page 23)

Lab Note: Be sure the setup for this activity is done on a fireproof surface.

Data and Observations

Lab Note: Temperatures will vary, but the temperature change will usually be greater for the peanut and wood splint than for the marshmallow.

Possible observations:

Peanut: Oil drops from peanut as it burns; some smoke and odor produced; black charcoal-like residue in shape of peanut remains after burning. Marshmallow: Some smoke and odor produced as it burns; black mass with gooey white center left as residue. Wood splint: Little smoke or odor produced as it burns; small amount of gray-black ash left.

Questions and Conclusions

1. Answers may vary, but in most cases the marshmallow did not raise the water temperature as much as the wood or peanut.
2. The marshmallow caused the most smoke; the wood caused the least.
3. The wood burning caused less odor than the peanut or marshmallow.

4. The wood left less residue than the other two samples.
5. The marshmallow, because it produced smoke and odor, left a gooey residue, and heated the water less.

Chapter 6   Views of Earth

Laboratory Activity 1 (page 27)

Questions and Conclusions

1. The average can be obtained by adding the three trials and dividing the sum by the number of trials.
2. The observed latitude might vary by a few degrees from the actual latitude.
3. Variations might result because the students' sextants are not as precise as the sextants sailors use. Also, students' measurements might not be accurate.
4. increased accuracy

Lab Note: You might wish to have students discuss how a ship's captain could tell if the ship were drifting east or west from the course. A captain could use the position of the Sun or stars to determine the east-west course.

Laboratory Activity 2 (page 31)

Data and Observations

1. 75° West
2. 165° East
3. will vary depending on map
4. will vary depending on map
5. 7
6. west

Questions and Conclusions

1. 11,270 km; Distance = map scale x map distance between Washington, DC, and Wake Island
2. 11,270 km ÷ 1,127 km/h = 10 h
3. 120°
4. 11 A.M.
5. 6 P.M.
6. yes
7. No, the plane left Washington, DC, at 8 A.M. and traveled westward—the same direction as the Sun.

Lab Note: You might wish to have students research and report on the Greenwich System of World Time Zones.

Chapter 7   Weathering and Soil

Laboratory Activity 1 (page 33)

Data and Observations

Copper strip—bright copper color; green Beaker $FeSO_4$—clear; rusty with flakes in it

Questions and Conclusions

1. The acid cleaned the copper.
2. chemical
3. The copper turned green.
4. The copper, carbon dioxide, and moisture in the air react with the clean porous surface of the copper.

5. Iron reacts with oxygen to form iron (III) oxide (Fe_3O_3). Water acts like a catalyst.
6. chemical
7. The stains result when iron minerals in the rocks react with oxygen in air or water.
8. The soil may prevent moisture, acids, and gases from reaching and reacting with the bedrock.

Lab Note: You might have students explain what would happen to a copper penny buried in soil. It would quickly turn green because the soil contains oxygen, water, and carbon dioxide. If sulfur were present, the penny might turn black.

Laboratory Activity 2 (page 35)

Questions and Conclusions
1. No. Infiltration is fastest in the gravel and almost imperceptible in the clay.
2. In wet soil. In dry soil, water clings to soil particles until they become saturated.
3. The clay layer infiltrates most slowly. It took the water the longest time to pass through the layer.
4. The gravel layer is most likely to be a bad filter. You could rerun the experiment four times, each time using the same amount of water and one of the filtration substances.

Chapter 8   Erosional Forces

Laboratory Activity 1 (page 37)

Data and Observations
Answers will vary with students' results.

Questions and Conclusions
1. creep—slow
2. mud flow—rapid
3. the slope of the stream table
4. landslide—rapid
5. mudflow; the water saturates the loosely patched soil and rock. The entire mass of debris then moves down the slope.
6. mudflow. A mudflow moves suddenly, carrying automobiles and houses and burying roadways. the movement of creep is so slow that it causes only minor surface disturbances. Vegetation holds the soil in place fairly well.
7. Vegetation is planted; walls are built to block slides; water drainage is improved.

Laboratory Activity 2 (page 39)

Questions and Conclusions
Valley glaciers begin as snowfields that form where the snowfall is heavy and temperatures are cold enough for the snow to remain throughout the year. When the accumulation reaches a depth of 30–60 meters, the bottom layers become ice and the mass begins to move down the valley. Valley glaciers make the landscape more rugged. They form peaks called horns, U-shaped valleys, and hanging valleys.

Lab Note: You may want to have students model an area that was covered by a continental glacier. The lake area of Minnesota and the upper New York State area are good examples. Students could work from topographic maps.

Chapter 9   Water Erosion and Deposition

Laboratory Activity 1 (page 41)

Data and Observations
Part A

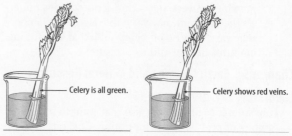
Celery is all green.   Celery shows red veins.

Part B

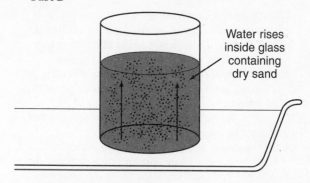
Water rises inside glass containing dry sand

Questions and Conclusions
1. When the water reaches the glass of dry sand, it is drawn up into the sand.
2. The colored water is drawn into the celery through the cell walls of the plant tissue.
3. The red food color shows in the fibers of the celery. Veins show the location of the openings in the plant tissues
4. Water molecules would move upward from the zone of saturation toward the top of the sand. Capillary action would not be as effective in a desert because the water table is so far below the surface.
5. the most effective capillary action would take place in fine sandstone

Laboratory Activity 2 (page 43)

Lab Note: Two well-known limestone caverns are the Carlsbad Caverns in New Mexico and Mammoth Cave in Kentucky.

Data and Observations
Lab Note: Warm soda should be room temperature.

Table 1
on ice—slow escape of CO_2; warm—almost explosive escape of CO_2; limewater—turns milky

Questions and Conclusions

1. carbon dioxide
2. gas escaped; The carbon dioxide gas in the cans is under pressure. When the pressure is decreased (when the can is opened), the gas escapes.
3. the warm can; The gas expands and is more active when the liquid is warm.
4. As the carbon dioxide escaped from the soft drink can, it caused calcium carbonate to precipitate from the limewater.
5. The calcium carbonate is deposited as stalactites on the roof of the cave.

Lab Note: You may have students report on one of the limestone caves mentioned in the first Lab Note.

Chapter 10   Plate Tectonics

Laboratory Activity 1 (page 45)

Lab Note: It is unlikely that any two maps will be exactly the same. Map should be fairly split on the interpretation of location X as land or water.

Questions and Conclusions

1. Most students will indicate that it was land because it is located between places where fossils of small mammals and dinosaurs were found.
2. Answers will vary, because it is located between areas where fossils of land organisms and ocean organisms were found.
3. Because it is located between areas where fossils of land organisms and ocean organisms were found, some students will make it land while others will make it ocean. You could only know for sure if you found Mesozoic fossils at that location.
4. Answers will vary, depending on where students drew the shoreline of the land near location H.
5. The continent must have moved. During the Mesozoic it must have been located near the equator for corals to have grown in the oceans.

Laboratory Activity 2 (page 49)

Data and Observations

Students' data will vary. When observing the bubbles at the beginning of the experiments, students should notice that the bubbles tend to collect under the pieces of foam and coalesce. Bubbles will grow larger and larger until they slip to the sides of the foam and escape. Where two pieces of foam are touching, the bubbles will escape fairly vigorously. Eventually they will almost explode or pop. This action should lead students to consider the pressure and activity of magma and volcanoes at continental plate margins. When students observe the movement of their foam pieces during a full boil, they should see that the pieces are circulated from the center of the pot up to the top and out to the sides of the pot. There they will either get stuck or recirculate. Either way it is important that students draw inferences about the behavior and motion of crustal plates from the activity of their foam continents.

At the end of the experiment most students will not see much change in their foam continents. They should conclude that unlike real plates, the foam ones did not melt or break apart.

Questions and Conclusions

1. The bubbles were stuck under the foam. They grew together and formed one large bubble. Then the large bubbles floated to the sides of the foam where they burst up between two pieces of foam.
2. The action of the bubbles is similar to that of a volcano. The bubbles were like magma that increases in pressure at weak points along plate boundaries. It escapes like the bubbles in an explosion.
3. At first it seemed as though the foam went all over the place. After a while, the pattern was noticeable: the foam went down at the sides of the pot and up in the middle of the boiling water.
4. The tectonic plates move along the hot liquid mantle just like the foam. When they cannot move any farther they get stuck, like the Indian plate, or go under, like the Pacific plate.
5. This experiment is different because the foam never changed shape or cracked. In the real world, the plates change according to the kinds of forces acting on them. As a result, the plates of crust are moved by convection currents and broken up on the boiling surface of the mantle.
6. If the convection currents in the mantle changed direction or stopped, the tectonic plates would also stop. Everything would stay right where it is. Volcanoes and earthquakes might stop.

Chapter 11   Earthquakes

Laboratory Activity 1 (page 53)

Lab Note: Student maps may vary slightly. A few of the earthquake observations are purposely ambiguous and can be given different values by the students. In general, the pattern is a bull's-eye centered on the towns of Split Rock and Victor.

Data and Observations
Table 2

1. II		15. VI	
2. IV		16. IV	
3. II		17. V	
4. IV		18. VI	
5. IV		19. VII	
6. I		20. V	
7. V		21. V	
8. V		22. IV	
9. V		23. VII	
10. VI		24. III	
11. VI		25. III	
12. III		26. III	
13. III		27. IV	
14. II		28. VI	

Map of Earthquake Region
0   25km   50 km
Scale

Questions and Conclusions

1. The cities of Split Rick and Victor were closest to the epicenter. These cities had the greatest Modified Mercalli Scale values.
2. The zone with a rating of V is approximately 100 to 125 km wide.
3. Possible sources of error are the following: Damage to buildings may be more due to the soil or bedrock underneath them than how close they are to the epicenter. Some people may exaggerate their reactions. Some people may be more aware and observant than other people.

Laboratory Activity 2 (page 59)

Lab Note: You may wish to tie in this activity to the plate tectonics theory.

Data and Observations

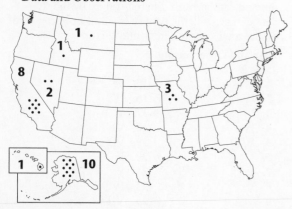

Questions and Conclusions

1. west of the Rocky Mountains, from California to Alaska; in Missouri

2. Eight earthquakes in Alaska, for the years 1964, 1957, 1965, 1938, 1958, 1899, 1899, and 1986, would all be classified as great since all had a magnitude of 8.0 or greater.
3. There must be faults in the underlying rock structure.
4. Answers will vary.
5. Answers will vary.
6. Yes. This was a very powerful earthquake, which would have caused a lot of shaking, and the soil in the area was wet. When an earthquake shakes wet soil, liquefaction occurs.

Lab Note: Students may be interested in mid-continent earthquakes. You may wish to have students report on the New Madrid fault earthquakes. Students could also report on the San Andreas fault in California.

Chapter 12 Volcanoes

Laboratory Activity 1 (page 63)

Questions and Conclusions

1. Dried flower color is not as bright as fresh flower color. Dried flowers are stiff, not pliable like fresh flowers.
2. It was used as a drying agent.
3. Both silica powder and volcanic ash are drying agents.
4. sand
5. No. The flower must be buried, and a long period of time must pass before it is considered a fossil.

Laboratory Activity 2 (page 65)

Data and Observations

Students' should observe that the plaster begins to crack as the balloons expand.

Students' data in Tables 1 and 2 will vary. However, they should find that the radius of the debris field in Part A increases with the size of the balloon. In Part B, they should find that the diameter and height of the "volcano" increase as more toothpaste is added. They should also find that the diameter of the flow is much larger than its height.

Questions and Conclusions

1. The large balloons modeled magma under the greatest pressure. The large balloons contain the most air. The more air a balloon contains, the more it stretches and the greater the pressure inside it.
2. As the size of the balloon increased, so did the distance the pieces of plaster were thrown. The size of the balloon indicates the amount of pressure inside it, and the radius of the debris field indicates the force of the explosion. Therefore, the results show that as pressure in a volcano increases, so does the explosive force of an eruption.
3. The eruption modeled in Part A was explosive. Therefore, the volcano being modeled could be a cinder cone volcano or a composite volcano.

Cinder cone volcanoes throw tephra into the air as they erupt explosively, and composite volcanoes sometimes erupt violently by releasing large amounts of ash and gas.

4. The inflation of the balloons modeled the expansion of gases inside heated magma. The cracks in the plaster indicated the force of the pressure that builds up inside the volcano.

5. a. In general, the second layer of toothpaste flowed over the top of the first layer, and the third layer flowed over the second.

   b. This result suggests that the top layer of basaltic lava was deposited more recently than the layers underneath it.

6. The layers of toothpaste were much wider than they were tall. Shield volcanoes have this broad, flat shape.

7. The types of "lava" produced by each model were very different. In Model A, the pieces of plaster represented tephra thrown into the air by an explosive eruption. The "tephra" was solid and irregularly shaped. In Model B, the toothpaste represented basaltic lava. It did not fly through the air, but flowed smoothly over the cardboard. In Model A, the eruption happened quite suddenly, while the eruption of Model B occurred more slowly. In both models, newer layers of lava or tephra built up on top of older layers. In addition, pressure played a role in both eruptions.

Chapter 13   Clues to Earth's Past

Laboratory Activity 1 (page 69)

Questions and Conclusions

1. Layer A; It is on the bottom and, by the principle of superposition, is the oldest.
2. The beds have been folded upward into an anticline.
3. The folding predated the glaciation and subsequent deposition of the glacial till.
4. The glacier withdrew and vegetation was able to grow. Then a second advance occured.
5. no; The topography is too smooth; If the area had been mountainous it would have had valley glaciers; hanging valleys, horns, and steep walled valleys would be left.
6. two
7. Beds A,B, and C were deposited and then uplifted and folded into an anticline. Erosion removed bed C and part of Bed B from the top of the anticline. The area then was covered by a continental glacier that deposited a layer of till as it withdrew. During a period of warming and weathering, peat and soil were formed on the till. Another advance of the ice was followed by a retreat, and the second layer of till was deposited.

Laboratory Activity 2 (page 73)

Data and Observations

Students' sketches will vary with the objects they choose.

Questions and Conclusions

1. If a fossil appears in soils and rocks from many time periods, it does not isolate and identify when the organism existed.
2. Yes
3. Yes, both fossils are from the same type of organism
4. No, the soil in the bottom layer was laid down first. The fossils in the bottom layer are older than the fossils in the middle layer. A lived during both time periods.
5. what fossils are located in which layers of soil
6. Answers will vary Results should be similar. If the containers were disturbed during excavation, the fossils could have shifted. Results would be invalid
7. It is important to note that index fossils are found only during a specific time period. Fossils that are found nearby are close in age. If another like fossil is found from a different time, you can infer that the second plant or animal lived longer than the index fossil object. Whether the second fossil is found above or below or below the index fossil helps to determine time spans when that organism existed.

Chapter 14   Geologic Time

Laboratory Activity 1 (page 77)

Data and Observations

1. eye color, height, hair color, skin color—Students may think of others.

Table 1
Answers will vary.

Table 2
Answers will vary.

Questions and Conclusions

1. Height, upright walking, ability to communicate with each other with verbal and written languages are possible answers.
2. Answers will vary.
3. Answers will vary, but height should be somewhat shorter.
4. The members of the species have become taller.
5. By watching how one characteristic changes over time, scientists can date fossils.
6. The changes take place over a much longer time span (millions of years) when dealing with fossils.

Laboratory Activity 2 (page 79)

Lab Note: You may need to remind students that 1,000 million years equals 1 billion years.

Data and Observations

Table 1
Precambrian Time; 3.456 billion years or 3 billion, 456 million years
Paleozoic Era; 299 million years
Mesozoic Era; 180 million years
Cenozoic Era; 65 million years

Graph

Should show data accurately, making clear the enormous difference in the length of the Precambrian Era as compared with of the each of the other three Eras.

Timeline

Specific representations will vary slightly, but should clearly show the relative differences among the Eras. Art should be relative and pertinent to the Era with which it is associated.

Questions and Conclusions

1. Precambrian time is the longest division; the Cenozoic Era is the shortest division.
2. about 2.1 times longer
3. in the Cenozoic Era; in the Holocene Epoch
4. at least 30 times longer; exact answers will vary depending on numbers used for calculations.
5. Answers will vary, but might include that the most recent events were difficult to mark and illustrate because the time periods represent such a small part of the time line.

Chapter 15   Atmosphere

Laboratory Activity 1 (page 83)

Data and Observations

1. Bubbles rise through the water.
2. Pressure against hands; part of mattress surrounding hands rises.

Table 1—Answers will vary depending on the air mattress used.

Questions and Conclusions

1. Bubbles of air rose to the surface.
2. Air occupies space, and air is less dense than the water.
3. Volume of the mattress is determined by multiplying length × width × height.
4. It decreased.
5. It rose. This shows that air exerts pressure.
6. Yes; Air forced into a tire or balloon will exert pressure on the inside, causing the tire or balloon to expand. When the air mattress was depressed and released, air pressure returned it to its original shape.

Lab Note: You may have students list other examples of air pressure applications, such as airplane cabins, pneumatic drills, hair dryers, divers' suits, space suits.

Laboratory Activity 2 (page 85)

Questions and Conclusions

1. The direct rays of the Sun hitting the thermometer will cause the thermometer to become warmer than the air.
2. Students' answers will depend on their graphs.
3. Answers probably will agree. Students should observe lower temperatures in the morning and on cloudy days.

4. Air temperatures depend on the amount of solar energy absorbed by the land surface. The lowest temperature of the day usually will be just before sunrise. Cloud cover also will prevent some of the solar energy from reaching the surface.

Chapter 16   Weather

Laboratory Activity 1 (page 87)

Questions and Conclusions

1. The match went out when it hit the water. Smoke from the match rose up toward the mouth of the bottle.
2. The smoke from the match disappeared, and the air inside the bottle cleared.
3. When the bottle was released, a cloud formed.
4. The "clouds" formed by the hot water were denser than the ones formed by the cold water. Warm air above warm water holds more water than cold air above cold water.
5. When the bottle is no longer being squeezed, the pressure inside the bottle decreases. This also causes the temperature to decrease, or cool. This causes the water vapor inside the bottle to condense around the air particles.
6. The smoke from the match released tiny particles into the air in the bottle. These are the particles around which the water vapor condensed to form a "cloud."
7. Answers will vary, but should reflect an understanding of any differences between the hypothesis and the results.
8. Clouds form when warm air is forced upward, expands, and cools. As the air cools, the amount of water vapor needed for saturation decreases and the relative humidity increases. When relative humidity reaches 100 percent, the air is saturated and water vapor begins to condense. Condensation occurs in tiny water droplets around small dust or salt particles. Because these droplets are so small, they remain suspended in the air as clouds.

Laboratory Activity 2 (page 91)

Questions and Conclusions

1. Answers will vary. Most areas experience fluctuations in wind speed and direction. The amount of electricity would vary.
2. Answers will vary.
3. Wind provides a clean, free source of energy.
4. Wind speeds are not constant. Windmills constructed would interfere with the environment.

Chapter 17   Climate

Laboratory Activity 1 (page 95)

Data and Observations

1. Data will vary.

Questions and Conclusions

1. The air bottle had the greatest temperature change.

2. A large amount of heat energy can be absorbed by water so its temperature increase is relatively small. The water is able to absorb the heat from the Sun. The air does not absorb the heat energy like water. Its temperature will rise more quickly as a result of solar energy input.

3. The bottle with water is more like a warm, coastal climate. The bottle with air is more like the flat, inland climates.

4. The angle of incoming sunlight is less direct in the polar regions. As a result, the North and South Poles are always cold.

Laboratory Activity 2 (page 99)

Data and Observations Table

1. Data will vary, but data table and graph should show that the gravel lost heat more quickly than the water.

Questions and Conclusions

1. the gravel; The temperature increased at a faster rate.
2. the gravel; The temperature decreased at a faster rate.
3. water; The water stored more heat and released the heat at a slower rate.
4. 3726 L
5. Under the building in a crawl space is one possibility.
6. Add insulation around the storage container. Use a solid that is smaller than rocks but stores heat; for example, aluminum chips.

Chapter 18   Ocean Motion

Laboratory Activity 1 (page 103)

Questions and Conclusions

1. The salt would be carried in the water in solution.
2. Salt dissolved in the water would remain when the water evaporated.
3. solid deposits
4. Salt content could start to increase over time if there were fewer life forms in the oceans (perhaps due to pollution), and thus less use of salt, or if people caused more salt to be transported to the oceans.
5. Salt can "evaporate" from the seawater on windy days. You can "taste" the salt.

Laboratory Activity 2 (page 105)

Questions and Conclusions

1. in the saltwater
2. Objects float higher, or are more buoyant, in salt water than in freshwater.
3. Students should observe that the waterline on the boat is lower for the salt water.
4. Freshwater is less dense than salt water and will float on top of the salt water.
5. The greater the density, the greater the buoyant force.
6. Answers will vary. Most students should recognize that freshwater is less dense than salt water.
7. The liquids eventually will mix, and the density will become uniform throughout the entire liquid.

8. Fresh river water will remain at the surface for a short time. Eventually the water mixes.

Lab Note: You may wish to have students explain how a large cargo ship that is made of materials denser than water can float. Students could investigate the best design for such ships.

Chapter 19   Oceanography

Laboratory Activity 1 (page 107)

Questions and Conclusions

1. Answers will vary. With care, maps should be fairly accurate.
2. The map would probably show more details.
3. If a double set of readings were taken and then averaged, or if measurement marks were made on the string, the map might be more accurate.
4. The depth of the ocean floor would cause this method to be ineffective. Also, waves and currents would cause inaccuracies. In addition, the ocean is a big place. Mistakes in location are easy to make.

Laboratory Activity 2 (page 111)

Lab Note: For best results, check to see that bubbles are forming at the *Elodea's* cut end. If not, recut it and crush it again until the bubbles can be seen.

Data and Observations

Table 1
Data will vary.

Table 2
Data will vary.

Questions and Conclusions

1. a. Data will vary.
   b. Data will vary.
   c. Plants in the light will have produced noticeably more oxygen than plants in the dark.
2. A gas collected in the test tube over the plant in the light but not over the plant in the dark; the fact that no gas collected over the plant in the dark indicates that no photosynthesis took place.
3. There is no proof included in this experiment that the gas given off is oxygen. We assume that the gas is oxygen because photosynthesis is occurring.

Lab Note: The standard test for oxygen is to place a glowing (not flaming) wood splint into a test tube containing the unknown gas. The glowing splint will burst into flames if the gas is oxygen. Perform the test on the tubes of gas collected in this activity. **WARNING:** *Wear safety glasses. Have all nearby students wear safety glasses.*

4. Carbon dioxide is one of the substances that plants use in photosynthesis. The sodium bicarbonate is the source of the carbon dioxide in this experiment.
5. The *Elodea* used the water in the jar, the carbon dioxide produced when the baking soda dissolved in water, and light from the lamp for photosynthesis.

6. The energy is stored in the plant. The oxygen is captured in the test tube.

7. **a.** The plants produced oxygen for the first 11 hours and then again for the 6 hours from hour 18 through hour 24, for a total of 17 hours. This indicates that the plant received light for 17 hours.

   b. Only a very small amount of oxygen was produced in the 7 hours from hour 11 through hour 18. This indicates the plant was in the dark for these 7 hours.

8. **a.** The plant produced about 45 mL of oxygen each hour for the first 11 hours. When it was next exposed to light, from hours 18 through 24, it produced about 27 mL of oxygen each hour.

   b. The plant probably was exposed to more light during the first 11 hours than during the last 7 hours. The difference in sunlight on a sunny day versus a cloudy day might explain this difference.

   c. A similar difference in sunlight would produce a similar difference in the amount of oxygen produced. A cloudy day might produce this difference in ocean plants that are near the surface. In addition, less sunlight is available to plants that are farther from the surface, so distance from the surface could explain the difference in oxygen production.

9. Green plants provide food for the ocean animals to consume and oxygen for their respiration.

Chapter 20   Our Impact on Land

Laboratory Activity 1 (page 115)

Questions and Conclusions

1. prevents infiltration, adds calcium carbonate to adjacent areas, reflects heat and light, adds lead poison to strip along roads, destroys wildlife habitat

2. It adds hydrocarbon gases (carbon monoxide) to the atmosphere, as well as some smoke.

3. bicycling, walking, driving newer cars with anti-pollution equipment, taking public transportation, such as trains or buses

4. Answers will vary. Possibilities include local industries, cars, and burning of dumps.

5. Answers will vary. Possibilities may include scrubbers on smokestacks to remove some gases, electronic air cleaners to remove some particulate matter, or using less fossil fuels.

6. Possibilities include granite, limestone, or sandstone blocks and clay, gravel for concrete or asphalt, wood, petroleum products.

7. farming areas, resources of sand, gravel, clay, recreation areas, wood, wooded/natural areas, nature preserves/wildlife habitats.

8. Alternatives include leaving green areas in cities and zoning certain areas for recreation and/or farming or nature preserves. Students may also think of others.

9. Answers will vary; most drawbacks involve cost.

Laboratory Activity 2 (page 119)

Data and Observations

Table 1

Top row: blue, no change, clear solution
Second row: clear, turns red, copper coating on iron

Questions and Conclusions

1. The copper(II) sulfate dissolves in water and makes available copper ions.

2. The iron provides a means to extract the copper from the solution.

3. A chemical reaction is being used.

4. Sulfuric acid is formed.

5. No; iron and sulfuric acid remain.

6. The stream might become too acidic for fish and water plants to exist. Most copper mines try to find a market for the sulfuric acid.

7. Heavy rain would dissolve the copper (II) sulfate and carry it into streams or into underground water.

Chapter 21   Our Impact on Water and Air

Laboratory Activity 1 (page 121)

Lab Note: The distillation apparatus is available from some garden catalogs and plant stores.

Data and Observations

Table 1
Student answers will vary

Questions and Conclusions

1. it decreased

2. The drops of water condensed from the water vapor inside the plastic bag.

3. evaporation, condensation; heat from the sun or sunlamp

4. use various tests: litmus for acids, phenolphthalein for carbonates

5. clean plastic, shovel, clean container

Laboratory Activity 2 (page 123)

Data and Observations

1. Students answers will vary.

2. Students answers will vary.

3. Students answers will vary. Accept all reasonable answers.

Questions and Conclusions

1. Students answers will vary, but will tend to indicate winter months.

2. Students answers will vary, but will tend to indicate summer months.

3. The energy of the Sun can cause chemical reactions in certain air pollutants, producing smog. The Sun's energy is most direct upon Earth's surface in the summer months.

4. Vacations during the summer months contribute to poor air quality. As more drivers are on the road, more pollutants are released into the air.

5. Student answers will vary. Accept all reasonable answers.

6. People with allergies, asthma, immune system disorders, and upper respiratory disorders might make up part of the sensitive group. Children and the elderly might be in this group as well.
7. Students answers will vary.

Chapter 22   Exploring Space

Laboratory Activity 1 (page 125)

Lab Note: The number of stars visible at any one time from one place may vary greatly. Usually, the number does not exceed one or two thousand.

Data and Observations

Diagrams will vary. Landmarks should be included and labeled. Stars and colors should be recorded.

Questions and Conclusions

1. apparent brightness, color; All stars "twinkle" and seem to occupy fixed positions in the sky. Students may suggest other properties they used.
2. Answers will vary. Most stars fit into one of the seven spectral types given at the beginning of this activity.
3. G
4. 5000–6000 K
5. 4727–5727°C

Laboratory Activity 2 (page 127)

Data and Observations

Answers will vary, depending on the size of the hemisphere used.

Questions and Conclusions

1. Right ascension lines pass through the celestial poles; Right ascension is measured in hours, minutes, and seconds.
2. Both are measured in degrees. Declination gives the location of a star above or below the celestial equator.
3. the prime meridian
4. Different stars are visible because as Earth revolves around the Sun, different parts of the sky become visible to us.
5. These stars are below the horizon.

Chapter 23   The Sun-Earth-Moon System

Laboratory Activity 1 (page 129)

Data and Observations

Table 1—Answers will vary depending on the accuracy of the student.
Table 2—You may wish to have students show their velocity calculations.

Questions and Conclusions

1. the point on the equator
2. the point at 60° N
3. the point on the North Pole
4. the latitude or the distance north or south of the equator
5. The linear velocity decreases from the equator to the poles.

Laboratory Activity 2 (page 131)

Data and Observations

Students' drawings will vary but should demonstrate an understanding of the activity.

Questions and Conclusions

1. Students should note that only the tip of the cardboard is visible at first, then the complete triangle is visible.
2. As a ship approaches from across the ocean, the top of the ship comes into view first, followed by the remainder of the ship.
3. The tip of the cardboard comes into view first because the cardboard is moving over a curved surface—the basketball. Similarly, the top of the ship at sea comes into view first because the ship is moving over a curved surface—Earth.
4. Students should note that the shadow cast by the textbook was rectangular while the shadow cast by the basketball was round.
5. If Earth were flat, its shadow would look like a flat "bar" on the moon during a lunar eclipse. Instead, Earth casts a curved shadow on the moon.
6. The basketball, a round object, casts a curved shadow. The textbook, a flat object, casts a sharp-edged shadow. Thus, Earth's curved shadow on the moon during a lunar eclipse is evidence of Earth's round shape.
7. Answers will vary. Students may mention photographs of Earth from space or their own observations of other objects in space, such as the Sun and moon. Accept all reasonable answers.

Chapter 24   The Solar System

Laboratory Activity 1 (page 133)

Table 1
Answers will vary, but data should show higher temperatures with the lid on.

Questions and Conclusions

1. The lid reflected the heat back into the box; no heat could escape into the air.
2. Some of the solar energy that reaches Earth's surface is trapped by carbon dioxide gas. This process heats the atmosphere near the surface.
3. The lid prevents the longwave radiation from escaping by absorbing some of the energy. On Earth some energy leaks back to space.
4. Sunlight striking Venus's surface is absorbed and reradiated as longwave radiation. The atmosphere, rich in CO_2, traps this radiation close to the planet's surface, thus heating it.
5. Carbon dioxide present in both atmospheres absorbs the reradiated energy from the surface. The atmosphere of Venus is more dense, however, and more heat is retained by the large amounts of carbon dioxide.

Laboratory Activity 2 (page 137)

Data and Observations

Students' observations will vary depending on how well they performed the experiment. Most should observe that the wind from the fan blew beads of melting water away from the fan. If the fan was strong enough it should have blown some sand particles along with the water. However, it is important that the students observe that the water was ejected farther from the fan than the sand because of the density. An astute student will recognize the pattern between a dwindling comet tail and the water pattern on the paper.

Questions and Conclusions

1. They were both blown away from the fan. The water moved the farthest.
2. Wind from the fan was powerful enough to eject water and sand particles from their original position. The particles were always thrown away from the wind source.
3. The solar wind comes from the Sun in every direction. As the comet nears the Sun, the hot solar wind melts the ice in the comet. The melted ice and dust it held are forced behind the comet, away from the Sun. This is why the tail of a comet always points away from the Sun.
4. The dust and water from a comet fly off into space where they float around as cosmic debris. Because it is so cold in space, the water freezes back into ice crystals.
5. Yes. It is possible that when its orbit is far from the Sun, the comet will attract dust and water crystals from space. However, this would not be enough to keep it from eventually dying out or crashing into a planet or moon.

Chapter 25   Stars and Galaxies

Laboratory Activity 1 (page 141)

Data and Observations

Students' data will vary depending on the relative brightnesses of the flashlights used.

Hypothesis for the Dispersal of Light

The closer the flashlight, the more intense, or brighter, the light because the rays of light do not disperse as far, hence the circle of light appears to grow smaller as the distance decreases.

Questions and Conclusions

1. The farther from the wall, the dimmer the light, because the light—shown from that point—is scattered widely, or diffused. Brightness, or intensity, decreases when distance is increased.
2. The light increased in brightness, or intensity, as distance decreased. When the light focuses, or concentrates, on a smaller space, it is not diffused, so it appears to shine more brightly.
3. The closer the star, the brighter it will appear, because its light will not be diffused, or scattered.

4. Repeating the experiment with a bigger and brighter flashlight would result in recording a greater intensity of light at the farthest distance. This is because the absolute magnitude of the brighter flashlight is greater. It will give off more light, so more light reaches the wall with greater intensity; hence, light shown from the same distance as the weaker flashlight will also have a greater apparent magnitude.
5. Position the student with the weak light close to the wall so that its apparent magnitude is strong—the circle of light is intense, or bright. Then position the student with the strong flashlight farther from the wall, until the two circles of light nearly match in intensity. At this point, one could say that they share the same apparent magnitude, even though the stronger flashlight, of course, has the greater absolute magnitude.
6. Position both students at the same distance and compare the circles of light each casts on the wall. The stronger flashlight, with the greater absolute magnitude, will also have the greater apparent magnitude.
7. Answers will vary. Students may mention comparing the star to others, using what they know about other objects in the night sky, or even using parallax. It is always good to study an object over a long period to detect changes and to learn more about it.

Laboratory Activity 2 (page 145)

Lab Note: Discuss the meanings of *spectrum* and *spectral analysis*. Introduce the cut-outs on page 15 of the lab with students and review how each cut-out will be used in the lab.

Data and Observations

Table 1

A—iron, calcium, sodium, hydrogen, helium
B—iron, sodium, hydrogen; the standard
C—iron, sodium, hydrogen; answers will vary.
D—iron, sodium, hydrogen, mercury; answers will vary.

Questions and Conclusions

1. Student answers will vary; Red, as there are a lot of lines in the red wavelengths.
2. B, C, and D. It should be noted that Star D has the same composition, but the spectral lines are slightly shifted to the red wavelengths.
3. Star D's spectral lines are shifted toward the red part of the spectrum. The star is moving away from the observer.
   Lab Note: You might review the Doppler effect with students.
4. Star C's spectral lines are wider than star B's.
   Lab Note: This could be caused by any one of the reasons given in the paragraph above.